ASL
American Sign Language

Literature Series

Bird of a Different Feather

&

For a Decent Living

STUDENT WORKBOOK

SAM SUPALLA & BEN BAHAN

American Sign Language Literature Series
Series Editors: BEN BAHAN, SAM SUPALLA

Back cover photo credits:

First row:

VOICES OF THE ANIMALS. (1930). *Charles Krauel: A Profile of a Deaf Filmmaker*. DawnPictures.

FREDA NORMAN. (1972). *My Third Eye*. Courtesy of National Theatre of the Deaf.

NATHIE MARBURY. (1990). *Once Upon A Time...Children Classics Retold in ASL*. DawnPictures.

Second row:

ELLA MAE LENTZ. (1991). The National Anthem, *Signing Naturally Series*. DawnPictures.

JOE VELEZ. (1968). Jabberwocky, *Tyger! Tyger! And Other Burnings!* Courtesy of National Theatre of the Deaf.

MY THIRD EYE. (1972). Courtesy of National Theatre of the Deaf.

Third row:

SILENT WHISPERS. (1929). *Charles Krauel: a Profile of a Deaf Filmmaker*. DawnPictures.

THREE BLIND MICE. (1972). Courtesy of National Theatre of the Deaf.

BERNARD BRAGG. *(1968)*. Flowers in the Moonlight on the Spring River. (1968). *Tyger! Tyger! And Other Burnings!* Courtesy of National Theatre of the Deaf.

ISBN-13: 978-1-58121-054-5

ATTENTION: SCHOOLS & DISTRIBUTORS

Quantity discounts for schools and bookstores are available.
For information, please contact:

DawnSignPress
6130 Nancy Ridge Drive
San Diego, CA 92121-3223
(858) 625-0600 V • (858) 625-2336 FAX
(858) 768-0428 VP
Visit us at www.dawnsign.com

TABLE OF CONTENTS

PART 2 THE VALLEY

For a Decent Living

INTRODUCTION

THE *American Sign Language Literature Series* is designed to provide an unprecedented way to study and appreciate the oral-based literary works of the deaf community in the United States. The *ASL Literature Series* will not only enhance your comprehension and appreciation of ASL literature, but it will also guide you through the art of narrative expression and provide you with an insight into the deaf experience.

The *ASL Literature Series* is made up of two components: a Student Videotext and Student Workbook. The two narratives as told in your student videotext are signed by the original oral literary artists: *Bird of a Different Feather* by Ben Bahan and *For a Decent Living* by Sam Supalla. The accompanying student workbook allows you to study these narratives divided into structural units: strophes, topic units, chapters, and parts. The *ASL Literature Series* requires you to complete a wide range of activities both inside and outside of the classroom including the following:

- Comprehension Check
- Language Notes
- Background
- Literary Questions
- Retelling
- Anecdotes

You will also have the opportunity to appreciate signed literature beyond the scope of the narratives by understanding the background of the Signers.* Your instructor will show you a videotaped interview with the Signers as a basis for further discussion on the origins and development of the two narratives.

We feel confident that you will enjoy the *ASL Literature Series*.

---

* Signers with a capital "S" refers to literary artists who perform in ASL and whose works involve various genres within the oral traditions of the deaf community.

HOW TO USE THE VIDEOTEXT AND WORKBOOK

The Student Workbook is primarily designed as a guide to the videotext, to be utilized for homework assignments outside the classroom. Your study should begin outside the classroom and will prepare you for in-class activities.

Study begins with the first chapter, "The Eggs" in *Bird of a Different Feather* broken down into Part 1, "The Mountain" and Part 2, "The Valley" and has a total of nine chapters. You are expected to study one chapter at a time, as you will need to return to the classroom and discuss each chapter before studying further. You should not advance in the videotext until the teacher instructs you to do so.

In order to begin the assignment on the first chapter, you will watch Strophe 1 on the Student Videotext and answer the comprehension check questions in the Student Workbook. These questions are followed by language notes relevant to the strophe. Included in the language notes are photos designed to help develop your sensitivity to sign production, facial expression, and style of the Signer. Special attention is placed on how roleplaying (e.g., narrator vs. character) operates in ASL with relevant eye gaze/body shifting behaviors. At the end of each chapter, you will need to read the background information to help you develop an appreciation of the events in the chapter.

Upon completion of the chapter, you will also need to complete the literary questions on a separate piece of paper and turn them in as instructed. The comprehension check questions will be corrected by classmates during specified class sessions. Be sure to bring your workbook to class when necessary.

Based on your instructor's assignments, you will continue your study of each chapter with a discussion in the classroom. The success of these literary discussions and your other classroom activities depends on your completion of the homework assignments.

In addition to the literary discussions, there will be several retelling assignments videotaped in class to provide you with the instructor's feedback. Anecdotes related to the chapter studied will be shared in ASL by both the instructor and you. Your participation both in and out of class will be monitored by the instructor. There will be an examination covering Part 1 of the narrative and Part 2 (i.e., cumulative).

The second narrative, *For a Decent Living,* has a total of six chapters. The study procedure described for the first narrative is the same for the second. There will be an examination covering the entire narrative including a comparison between the two narratives.

Bird of a Different Feather

*B*ird of a Different Feather, as told by Ben Bahan, is best described as an allegorical fable: its lesson contains clear parallel meanings to deaf-related issues and events. The eagle family in the story represents a typical American family with one bird-child that is unlike the rest of the family. Aggravated with the continued denial of his true self, the bird has an identity crisis. A parallel can be made to a deaf child born into a non-signing family.[1]

The Signer has gone beyond the narrative and developed social and political commentary.[2] *Bird of a Different Feather* is told from the point of view of an omniscient author, or an all-knowing Signer. The Signer could have chosen to tell the narrative from the first person point of view, meaning the perspective of the protagonist bird, but the overall allegorical meaning of the narrative would then be shifted to the deaf individual's personal experience.[3] Rather, as an omniscient author, the Signer attempts to remain neutral, thus making his points more effectively. Ultimately, the Signer uses a form of literary satire which involves humor and wit to criticize the present system and how it handles deaf children and their hearing families.[4]

In this narrative, you will learn some relevant deaf-related issues and gain a better understanding of what some deaf children experience in their crucial formative years. In the videotape, the first chapter, "The Eggs," introduces you to the strange world that the protagonist is born into.

• • •

PART 1
THE MOUNTAIN

CHAPTER 1
THE EGGS

CHAPTER 1	
THE EGGS	
Topic Unit	
1	2
The Family	The Doctor
Strophes	
1-8	9-13

Comprehension Check

Strophe 1

1) What is the setting?

The Mountains

2) What is the character doing?
   - a) watching sports on T.V.
   - b) reading the sports page of a newspaper
   - c) reading a sports magazine
   - d) none of the above

Strophe 2

1) T/F- Mama Eagle runs into the room.   Wife

2) What does Mama Eagle say?
   - a) something just happened
   - b) something will happen soon
   - c) something is happening now
   - d) nothing is happening

3) T/F- Papa Eagle's response is one of interest and excitement.

5

Strophe 2 (cont'd)   Time Code

The Signer takes the role of Mama Eagle who runs quickly; her face expressing frenzy.   8.8

The Signer continues in the role of Mama Eagle. Stopping, Mama Eagle taps Papa Eagle's shoulder frantically to get his attention.   9.9

The Signer takes the role of Papa Eagle, who is responding to Mama Eagle's news. Papa Eagle is asking, "Really?"   13.7

Strophe 3

1) When Mama Eagle and Papa Eagle go into the next room, what do they see?
   - a) five eggs, ready to hatch
   - b) four eggs, ready to hatch
   - c) five eggs, hatching
   - d) four eggs, hatching

Time Code

The Signer takes the role of the narrator in describing Papa Eagle's feelings. Papa Eagle is thrilled about the eggs.

15.3

The Signer describes the characters moving about in their house. Papa and Mama Eagle run into the room together.

15.8

Strophe 3 (cont'd)

The Signer takes the role of the parents. Both Mama and Papa Eagle look at the eggs which are projected in front of the characters.   17.9

Strophe 4

1) T/F- The first eaglet is described as having big, blinky eyes.

2) What does Mama Eagle call the first eaglet?
      a) sweet
      b) red
      c) funny
      d) cute

The Signer takes the role of Mama Eagle, who gazes back to Papa Eagle.   32.0

Strophe 4 (cont'd)

The Signer takes the role of the eaglet. One head breaks the shell and pops out of the egg.

34.1

The Signer takes the role of Mama Eagle who hugs Papa Eagle affectionately.

40.4

Strophe 5

1) T/F- Three more eaglets emerge from their shells.

2) What do Mama and Papa Eagle say when the eggs hatch?
   a) "Aren't they cute!?"
   b) "Wow! This is a special day."
   c) "We are so lucky!"
   d) None of the above.

Strophe 6

1) What is the situation with the last egg?

2) T/F- Mama and Papa Eagle look at the hatched eggs and then back to the last egg.

Time Code

The Signer takes the role of Papa Eagle, and the character speaks to himself. He is wondering why nothing has happened.

57.2

Strophe 7

1) T/F- Only Papa Eagle is watching the egg closely.

2) What happens to the egg before the eaglet emerges?
        a) It cracks.
        b) Papa Eagle reaches in to pull the baby bird out.
        c) Both Mama and Papa Eagle help by sawing the egg.
        d) None of the above.

10

Strophe 7 (cont'd)   Time Code

The Signer takes the role of the narrator and tells the audience about the last egg. There is a feeling of relief.   1:04.2

Strophe 8

1) What is the problem with the last eaglet?

2) What is similar among all of the eaglets as described in this strophe?
        a) They all have green beaks.
        b) They all have the same color feathers.
        c) They all have big, blinky eyes.
        d) None of the above.

The Signer takes the role of Papa Eagle whose eyes are open wide with a feeling of exasperation. Papa Eagle responds directly to the hatching.   1:12.1

Strophe 9

1) Y/N- Are Mama and Papa Eagle happy?

2) T/F- Mama and Papa Eagle call their friends.

3) What mode of transportation does Doctor Eagle use when making his house call?

Strophe 10

1) What does Doctor Eagle use to examine the eaglet?

2) T/F- Mama and Papa Eagle express feelings of anxiety.

3) Why does Doctor Eagle examine the bird's beak?

Time Code

The Signer takes the role of narrator to describe Papa Eagle's concern about the last eaglet.

1:39.2

Strophe 10 (cont'd)

Time Code

The Signer takes the role of Doctor Eagle who has a feeling of unpleasant certainty.

1:50.4

Strophe 11

1) Why do Mama and Papa Eagle become upset?

2) What do Mama and Papa Eagle ask Doctor Eagle?
   a) what they should do
   b) what they should not do
   c) what the baby bird should do
   d) what the baby bird should not do

3) T/F- The doctor responds by telling them that the eaglet's health problems would be permanent.

4) How long should Mama and Papa Eagle wait until they see Doctor Eagle again?
   a) six weeks
   b) six months
   c) three weeks
   d) three months

Strophe 12

1) What are the eaglets doing during the argument?
        a) playing
        b) eating
        c) watching
        d) sleeping restlessly

2) How do they feel about the whole situation in general before their moment of resolution?

3) How do Mama and Papa Eagle reach their moment of resolve with each other?

Time Code

The Signer takes the role of Mama Eagle and reacts to the birth defect. She is blaming Papa Eagle angrily.

2:23.1

The Signer continues in the role of Mama Eagle and accuses Papa Eagle's ancestry of causing the birth defect.

2:25.1

Strophe 12 (cont'd)

The eaglets respond to the argument with jittery movements. The Signer takes the role of one eaglet and reacts as if he is in the middle of the argument.

2:30.2

Strophe 13

1) What do Mama and Papa Eagle do before going to bed?

The Signer takes the role of Mama and Papa Eagle as they go to bed; imitating their sleep.

2:49.6

Background: Identification of Deaf Children

The focus of the first chapter is on the eagle parents and how they identified one of their eaglets as different from themselves. The physical difference, which was clearly visible to the parents, was the shape of the beak. A doctor was called in to confirm the parents' discovery.

Although the characters in the narrative are not human, their circumstances are shared in a number of ways by hearing parents of deaf children. Unfortunately, however, there is one noted difference between the situations: early detection is difficult with deaf children, since hearing loss is not visible. This is further complicated by the fact that deaf infants display certain developmental milestones (e.g., vocal babbling) similar to hearing infants.

Parents are usually the first to suspect that their deaf child is not "normal." One source of identification lies in how the deaf child responds to vocalization or other sounds, as well as a delay in speech production. For example, the child may not speak his first words when expected. The parents may try to clap their hands or bang pots with a spoon behind their deaf child to confirm their suspicion.[5] The formal diagnosis of deafness, however, is conducted by a physician and usually occurs when the child is approximately 20 months old.[6] This delay is considered problematic by professionals in the field of deaf education as it involves the loss of a critical time period for various kinds of intervention.[7]

The experience that hearing parents have with their physician is often less than favorable. It has been reported that some parents feel resentment and frustration toward their physician for the way in which they were told about their child's deafness.[8] Physicians are not necessarily trained to deal with parents of deaf children and the decision-making process regarding their child. For a more supportive relationship, the physician should be compassionate to the parents. They should provide sufficient and accurate information to the parents.

In the narrative, the eagle parents reacted in a rather extreme manner when their physician told them the diagnosis. It was as if their dream of having a "perfect" child had collapsed, and they started to argue and blame each other. Although not all hearing parents cope with the diagnosis of a deaf child in the same way, they all experience strong emotions. Reactions typically include shock, denial, grief, anger and guilt.[9] These emotions usually emerge in stages over a period of time, and they have been compared to the grieving process one experiences after a death or a significant loss. The months following the diagnosis are difficult particularly for hearing parents of deaf children. These parents most likely encounter a variety of professionals who provide different and sometimes conflicting opinions, therefore making the decision-making process very difficult. Often parents also have the desire of making their child "normal" again. This, coupled with their emotions, vulnerability, and confusion, may lead to actions which are not always beneficial to the deaf child. Many hearing parents are also faced with a lack of a visually based linguistic system (i.e., signed language) that can affect their potential for effective parenting and socialization of their deaf child.[10]

Deaf parents, on the other hand, are usually more capable of accepting their child's condition. They are reportedly more successful at providing an emotionally healthy environment for the deaf child, and they "demonstrate more appropriate parental attitudes regarding independence and child management with deaf children."[11] With communication through ASL, deaf parents can rely on visually oriented strategies, such as consistent eye contact, for effective interaction with their deaf child.[12]

Although parents were once commonly told not to sign with their deaf children, the more recent problem lies in the lack of opportunities for hearing parents to learn and use ASL effectively, since signed language classes are not always readily available. Learning ASL as a second language also requires more than just taking classes; it includes a commitment to socialize through normal interaction with fluent signers (e.g., deaf adults). The same is true for deaf children, as they need to immerse themselves in an environment with fluent adult signers and deaf peers for normal language acquisition and socio-emotional development.

Using ASL as a language at home requires serious attention. It has yet to be systematically promoted by medical and educational institutions. If accepted and used readily, ASL can fulfill the language and communication needs of the entire family, as well as facilitating the process of accepting deafness for hearing parents.

More research and development are needed on how to serve families with young deaf children effectively, but some form of an early intervention may be required to create an appropriate, participative environment at home for the deaf child. With improved diagnosis procedures, the potential of deaf children for overall development may, in turn, be maximized during the critical formative years.

LITERARY QUESTIONS

1) Do you see anything to help establish the time frame of the story?

2) Discuss the irony of the doctor using a stethoscope to examine Straight Beak's beak. What does this particular behavior indicate about the medical profession?

3) Discuss the conflict that began after the hatching of Straight Beak and how it is resolved. What specifically did Mama and Papa Eagle do to each other?

4) What do the eagles symbolize in comparison to the rest of the bird world, including Straight Beak? Discuss the parallel, if any, where the deaf experience is concerned.

• • •

CHAPTER 2
SEARCH FOR A CURE

CHAPTER 2			
SEARCH FOR A CURE			
Topic Unit			
3 The Source	4 The Faith Healer	5 The Medicine Man	6 The Doctors
Strophes			
14-15	16-21	22-26	27-32

Comprehension Check

Strophe 14

1) Who is reading the *Enquirer*?

2) T/F- Eaglets awake to hear the news about a possible cure.

3) T/F- A minister is said to be capable of bringing about a miraculous change in Straight Beak.

Time Code

This sign is a product of *sign play*, a combination of the existing sign for "lying" and the "e" handshape representing the first letter of *Enquirer*.

2:53.4

Strophe 15

1) T/F- Papa Eagle responds to the possible cure with skepticism and resistance.

2) Y/N- Do both Mama Eagle and Papa Eagle decide that they should wait six months to see the doctor?

Time Code

The preacher and his work are described as worthy of consideration. The Signer, as the narrator, gazes at the audience and tells them directly what Mama and Papa Eagle are thinking.

3:09.2

The opportunity to see the preacher should be taken now. The Signer takes the role of Papa Eagle.

3:11.5

Strophe 15 (cont'd)

Mama Eagle takes Straight Beak on a train with a meandering route. The viewpoint is from all the characters on the train.

3:16.3

Strophe 16

1) T/F- The church that the eagle family attends is small.

2) T/F- All kinds of people are in line and in need of healing.

The church-goers stand in a long meandering line in front of the church.

3:22.1

Strophe 16 (cont'd)   Time Code

The Signer takes the role of an unknown   3:23.1
character who is limping in the line of
church-goers.

Strophe 17

1) T/F- Upon entering the church, the eagle family sees that it is less than half-full.

2) Y/N- Does an usher show the eagle family to their seats?

3) In order to meet with the minister, the eagle family has to:
      a) wait in their seats
      b) go behind the altar
      c) let the usher lead them
      d) stand in line for a long time

Inside the church, members are praising God   3:31.2
according to the "shakers and rollers"
custom. The Signer takes the role of these
church members and imitates their body
expression.

Strophe 17 (cont'd)

Time Code

The Signer takes the role of the church members and imitates their jumping with religious fervor.

3:33.6

Straight Beak, along with Mama Eagle, arrives at the altar of the church. The Signer becomes the narrator and tells the audience that the eagle family has reached their destination.

3:38.5

Strophe 18

1) What kind of bird is the preacher?
   a) chicken
   b) eagle
   c) duck
   d) ostrich

2) Describe the preacher's head.

3) T/F- The preacher's collar was described as glaring.

Strophe 19

1) Why does the preacher hold onto Straight Beak's beak?

2) Y/N- Does the preacher explain to anyone what he is doing?

The Signer takes the preacher's role who speaks "in a different tongue" to God.

3:48.6

The Signer continues in the preacher's role as he performs a ritual of holding Straight Beak's beak tightly.

3:55.1

Strophe 20

1) What is the result of the preacher's healing effort on Straight Beak?

2) What is the audience's response?
   a) hissing and booing
   b) singing and praising
   c) nothing–they are still trying to find their seats
   d) nothing–they had all left

Strophe 21

1) T/F- The preacher tells the family to buy their own Bible.

2) T/F- The preacher gives Mama Eagle the names of different books of the Bible to read.

3) Y/N- Do the parents take the preacher's advice?

The preacher tells the eagle family to have faith.

Time Code

4:15.6

Strophe 22

1) T/F- After the prayer, Straight Beak's beak bends only a little.

2) T/F- Mama Eagle and Papa Eagle hear a story of a medicine man in France who might be able to help them.

3) Y/N- Do the parents go and see the medicine man with Straight Beak?

Time Code

The Signer takes the role of the parents who are thinking of how time has passed with no success.

4:29.8

The Signer continues in the role of the parents who feel a lack of certainty and no direction, as the whole situation is floundering.

4:33.8

Strophe 23

1) What is the place like where the medicine man works?
        a) in a small house with a bare light bulb and windy
        b) under the hot sun with a blazing fire
        c) in a deep, winding canyon, near a river and very hot
        d) in a log cabin in the forest with rain and wind

2) T/F- Straight Beak is standing next to a fire.

3) Identify one item (other than a flower bud) that is thrown into the pot.

The Signer takes the role of the medicine man making a potion. A flower bud is plucked and thrown into the pot.

Time Code

4:57.1

Strophe 24

1) What does Straight Beak do all day?
        a) dances around the campfire
        b) nothing
        c) sits and watches everything
        d) stays inside while the parents talk

2) Where does the medicine man dance?

Strophe 24 (cont'd)   Time Code

The Signer takes the role of the medicine man who is performing a ritual by shaking instruments in his hands.   5:07.0

Strophe 25

1) What time of day does Straight Beak drink what was handed to him?
   a) early morning
   b) 12:00 noon
   c) mid-afternoon
   d) midnight

2) Y/N- Does this potion immediately change his beak?

The Signer takes the role of Straight Beak who is making an awful face.   5:15.0

Strophe 26

1) How often did the medicine man say that Straight Beak should drink the potion?
     a) morning and night, every day for the rest of his life
     b) morning and night for one week
     c) morning, noon, and night
     d) mornings for two weeks

2) T/F- Straight Beak vomits when he is given the medicine because it tastes so terrible.

Time Code

Straight Beak is repeatedly being spoon-fed the potion.

5:29.8

Strophe 27

1) How long had Mama Eagle and Papa Eagle tried different things?

2) Y/N- Did any of these tactics work on Straight Beak?

Strophe 28

1) What is the parents' next move with Straight Beak?
        a) see a doctor
        b) go back to the medicine man before seeing the doctor
        c) see two different doctors
        d) see three different doctors

Time Code

The Signer takes the doctor's role as he examines Straight Beak.

5:44.3

An operation is the only option. The Signer, still in doctor's role, explains what to do about the beak defect to Papa and Mama Eagle.

5:50.0

Strophe 28 (cont'd)   Time Code

Mama and Papa Eagle cannot afford surgery.   5:56.6

Strophe 29

1) T/F- The parents take Straight Beak to one more doctor.

2) What is the result of visiting doctors?
      a) They finally found the best doctor.
      b) They found one doctor who would not charge as much as the others.
      c) They found that all the doctors agreed on what had to be done.
      d) both b and c

3) T/F- The last doctor they see is an ear, nose and throat specialist (E.N.T.).

Papa and Mama Eagle take Straight Beak   6:04.7
from one doctor to another. The Signer takes
their roles and reacts to the uselessness of
seeing so many doctors.

Strophe 29 (cont'd)   Time Code

Mama and Papa Eagle are feeling discouraged.   6:09.0

Strophe 30

1) T/F- Straight Beak sits in the testing room with a window in front of him.

2) Why does Straight Beak raise his right and then left hand?

On the testing machine, two meters indicate the amplitude of the stimuli.   6:26.5

Strophe 30 (cont'd)

The Signer takes the role of Straight Beak who feels the vibrations on his beak from the probes and responds to the testing.

6:28.0

Strophe 31

1) What is the diagnosis given to Mama and Papa Eagle?
    a) Straight Beak is 100% eagle.
    b) Straight Beak is 100% straight-beaked.
    c) Straight Beak could feel the strong impulses sent to this beak.
    d) Straight Beak could not feel the strong impulses sent to his beak.

2) Y/N- Is the need for surgery consistent with the opinion of the E.N.T.?

3) How do the parents respond?

Strophe 32

1) What school is described?
    a) one that would train Straight Beak to be a doctor
    b) one that would train Straight Beak to become an eagle
    c) one that would help the parents to accept their child better
    d) one that would teach the parents how to turn their child into an eagle

2) T/F- Mama and Papa Eagle have heard of this school.

3) T/F- The ear specialist gives the parents the name of the school.

Strophe 32 (cont'd)

There is an alternative to surgery. The Signer takes the specialist's role and reassures Mama and Papa Eagle.

6:51.7

Straight Beak will be able to be among other eagles. The Signer continues in the specialist's role and explains to Mama and Papa Eagle the anticipated outcome of Straight Beak's education.

7:07.5

Both Mama and Papa Eagle are thrilled. The Signer takes the narrator's role to describe the characters' feeling.

7:17.6

Background: Two Views on Deafness – Pathological vs. Cultural

The eagle parents have decided to search for possible cures for Straight Beak. They have resolved to find a cure on their own rather than waiting for the physician to return. The search for a cure appears to be an act of desperation. The parents feel that Straight Beak is in dire need of being "fixed." Their underlying fear is that if no action is taken, Straight Beak will never be a part of the eagle world. The parents' actions–checking with the physician, medicine man, and faith healer–indicate that the eagle parents are instilled with the pathological (medical) point of view.

In the case of deaf children, the traditional view taken is also pathological. It exists across various social institutions, including medical, religious, and educational institutions.[13] Deaf children are widely regarded "...as a handicapped group whose inability to hear imposes severe limitations on how they can learn."[14]

Moreover, deaf children were once considered intellectually and cognitively inferior to hearing children. This conclusion was made erroneously and based on the idea of supremacy of spoken languages over signed languages. It was also widely believed that language was necessary for thought, and that without spoken language, a deaf child would not have the ability to think, conceptualize, and reason.[15] The implication for deaf children was that they needed to learn and use a spoken language exclusively and at all costs.

As a result, with professional advice, hearing parents often found themselves under pressure to make decisions related to possible surgery, use of hearing aids with deaf infants, and preparation for placing their deaf child in a pure, oral-education program. In short, according to the traditional pathological point of view, deaf children were "...flawed and somehow incomplete children, who must be made to look and act like hearing children."[16] Fortunately for deaf children, this negative image has begun to shift, as the pathological model loses ground and a cultural model takes over.

In recent years, signing with deaf children has become more accepted, and the notion of language being limited to the speech mode is dying. American Sign Language serves as an example of a signed language now widely recognized as a legitimate language in its own right and one that deaf children are capable of acquiring naturally leading to mastery.[17] However, this does not ensure that deaf children, especially of hearing parents, are exposed to ASL. In fact, hearing parents are often encouraged to learn a form of Manually Coded English (MCE) instead of ASL. Such artificial, English-based sign systems are widely believed to be as effective as ASL, and deaf children are expected to acquire and use MCE as they do ASL. However, in contrast to ASL, MCE lacks the critical element of naturalness, thus affecting the ease of learning and use of the system.[18]

The ongoing myth, that spoken language is required for thinking, is considered an extension of the pathological view on deafness. To critics, MCE represents the historical prejudice against the use of ASL with deaf children. Although deaf children may no longer be expected to speak like their hearing counterparts, their signing is still manipulated and dictated according to the rules of English.

In response to the traditional mind-set, which considers sign language a deficient version of spoken language, ASL is increasingly viewed as a legitimate and independent language. Just like English is a language, so are French, Chinese, and ASL. This view is called the cultural view, and is lauded in the deaf community. In this view, deaf speakers of ASL are viewed as a linguistic minority.

The implications are great. In Sweden, for example, Swedish Sign Language is now officially recognized alongside spoken Swedish. Hearing parents with a deaf child are quickly referred to an organization within the deaf community to learn the signed language.[19] Just like learning a foreign language, students of signed language are expected to learn another culture. Studying Swedish Sign Language, parents have formal contact with the deaf community, helping to foster their deaf child's overall development into a well-adjusted and functioning deaf adult.

The cultural view is also gaining acceptance in the United States. In fact, a form of bilingual education has been proposed for deaf children. It stresses the use of ASL as the primary language of instruction. English is then approached as a second language and is introduced through reading and writing.[20]

The basic argument in support of the cultural view lies in the nature of how deaf children learn the English language. The process is laborious–quite similar to learning a foreign language.[21] ASL should be their first language, as a natural language for deaf children which provides them with the language base necessary to access all subjects taught in the classroom.[22] English should be their second language. While there are a few schools that have adopted this bilingual education approach with their students, this movement marks a formal departure from the traditional pathological model of deaf education.

LITERARY QUESTIONS

1) What is the common attitude that you detect underlying all the treatments for Straight Beak?

2) How do you know Mama Eagle thinks Straight Beak's condition is severe? Discuss the decision by Mama Eagle to take Straight Beak to several different sources for a cure.

3) What did the Signer imply by repeatedly signing, "Still straight-beaked," in the chapter?

4) Is the recommendation to send Straight Beak to a special school a resolution of the conflict for the parents? How may it or may it not be satisfactory for the parents?

• • •

CHAPTER 3		
THE SCHOOL YEARS		
Topic Unit		
7	8	9
The School Philosophy	The Lessons	The Ambition
Strophes		
33-37	38-42	43-48

CHAPTER 3
THE SCHOOL YEARS

Comprehension Check

Strophe 33

1) T/F- The parents contact the school, and they are told to come over.

2) T/F- Straight Beak is taken to school.

Strophe 34

1) T/F- Mama Eagle and Straight Beak go into a classroom before going to see the principal.

2) Describe the principal's physical appearance.

3) What are the positions of Mama Eagle, Straight Beak and the principal?

$\boxed{M}$ = Mother $\boxed{SB}$ = Straight Beak $\boxed{P}$ = Principal

a)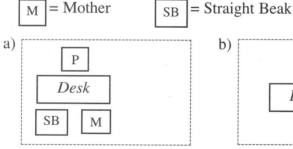

b)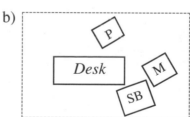

c)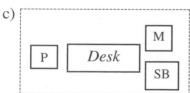

d)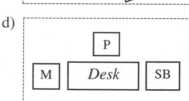

Strophe 34 (cont'd)   Time Code

The Signer takes the role of Mama Eagle   7:29.6
who takes Straight Beak's hand.

Strophe 35

1) What degree does the principal hold?
      a) straight beaks
      b) parroting
      c) nesting
      d) migration

2) Y/N- Was the principal given an award by the A. G. Bell Association honoring his achievements?

3) Y/N-Mama Eagle wants to impress the principal with Straight Beak's abilities.

The Signer takes the role of Straight Beak,   7:41.2
looking up at the principal's framed diploma.

Strophe 35 (cont'd)

The principal's background would indicate that he is very knowledgeable. The Signer narrates to describe what Straight Beak and Mama Eagle are thinking of the principal.

7:42.8

Strophe 36

1) T/F- The first thing that the principal explains is that straight-beaked birds can never survive in an eagle world.

2) What does the principal tell the parents about his school's probable effect on Straight Beak?

The Signer takes Mama Eagle's role and asks what the school philosophy is.

8:01.2

Strophe 37

1) What is Mama Eagle's reaction to the school's philosophy?

2) What is happening in the classroom?
      a) The children are sitting with colored blocks.
      b) The teacher is helping the children make crowns.
      c) Many other parents are sitting in another room watching the children.
      d) none of the above.

3) T/F- The other students all have the same color feathers as Straight Beak.

Time Code

The birds sit in a semi-circle. The Signer describes the diversity of the birds.

8:25.3

Strophe 38

1) T/F- The first thing the teacher says to Straight Beak is to sit down.

2) What is the first lesson?
      a) beak washing and polishing
      b) beak rubbing for curvature
      c) beak sharpening for hunting
      d) none of the above

3) Y/N- Is Straight Beak able to do the lesson without the teacher's demonstration?

Strophe 38 (cont'd)   Time Code

The Signer takes the role of narrator to tell   8:30.9
the audience that the chair is empty.

It is lesson time. The Signer takes the   8:34.7
teacher's role and begins teaching.

Strophe 39

1) What does the principal explain about the lesson?
    a) Young birds need to take advantage of their soft and flexible bodies to bend their beaks.
    b) Young bird's minds are soft and flexible, and they will learn to be eagles with time and practice.
    c) Young birds would win the hearts of the eagle community, which was, by nature, flexible and willing to accept change.
    d) both b and c

2) T/F- The parents think the explanation makes sense.

3) T/F- The parents leave the classroom right after the explanation.

Strophe 39 (cont'd)   Time Code

The Signer takes Mama Eagle's role and   9:11.9
responds to the lesson and its purpose. Mama
Eagle stands in awe.

Strophe 40

1) T/F- Straight Beak knows that his parents are leaving the room.

2) T/F- The class stopped right after the parents' departure.

Strophe 41

1) T/F- Straight Beak ends up staying at the school.

2) The principle behind the *next* lesson is:
        a) young birds could learn to fly
        b) the same principle as in the previous lesson
        c) young birds would be able to fly home one day
        d) none of the above

3) What is the expected result for Straight Beak's wings?

Strophe 42

1) What does Straight Beak keep practicing as he grows up?

2) T/F- Straight Beak is now ready to start college.

Strophe 43

1) What does the teacher ask the students to put down on paper?
      a) their current address
      b) their name
      c) their goals for future employment
      d) all of the above

2) T/F- The students are not able to write and draw pictures instead.

Strophe 44

1) What is the teacher's reaction after collecting the papers?
      a) extremely interested
      b) antagonized
      c) bored
      d) surprised

Time Code

The teacher's face shows her reaction. The Signer takes the narrator's role.

10:19.5

Strophe 45

1) How many papers does the teacher look at?

2) T/F- Every paper makes the teacher have a negative reaction.

3) Y/N- Does the teacher storm out of the classroom?

Time Code

The Signer narrates and describes the buildup of the teacher's emotions.   10:22.7

The teacher is "boiling mad." The Signer narrates and describes this negative reaction.   10:23.9

Strophe 46

1) What makes the teacher react as she does to her students?
      a) They want to enter military service.
      b) They do not know what their future employment will be.
      c) They put down that they want to go home and not have any future employment.
      d) They put down menial jobs for future employment.

Time Code

The Signer takes the teacher's role and bawls out everyone in the class.   10:38.0

The Signer continues in the teacher's role and criticizes their inferior job aspirations.   10:43.1

Strophe 46 (cont'd)   Time Code

The Signer continues in the teacher's role and argues with the students to change their goals. The teacher thinks the students are being "small-minded."   10:43.8

Strophe 47

1) T/F- The students react to the teacher with fear.

2) What does the first student write?

3) What does the teacher say to this?
   a) eagles never do that
   b) eagles are above doing that
   c) only poor low-lifes do that
   d) all of the above

The Signer continues in the teacher's role and believes that eagles are superior.   10:55.7

Strophe 47 (cont'd)

The second student wants to collect berries. The Signer (in the teacher's role) tells the student he cannot have such a career.

11:07.5

Strophe 48

1) How does the teacher demand that the class behave?

2) Y/N- Do the students submit to the demand?

3) What is the primary objective of vocational training?

Background: The Pure Oral Method

The philosophy and teaching approach in Straight Beak's school are quite similar to those of many deaf schools throughout history. The pure oral method, as this approach is commonly called, dominated the field of education from the 1880s to the 1970s. According to this method, deaf children were expected to be able to learn speech and lipreading skills in order to live in the hearing world. This proved to be a very difficult task for deaf children and has resulted in far more failures than successes. The pure oral method also relied on amplification of residual hearing, and the role of signed language was downplayed or outright prohibited.[23] This prohibition was based in the common fear that if a deaf child knew and used a signed language, this child would never want to learn to speak. Although this fear was never confirmed nor supported through research, it created a deep-seated suspicion of signed languages in general.

The experience that Straight Beak had in rubbing his beak and stretching his wings parallels that of deaf children undergoing speech lessons. Speech lessons for deaf children are made up of heavily structured and tedious drills. There is a chart of developmental sequences of elementary English sounds known as the Yale Chart. With this chart, deaf children are taught sounds one by one, learning how they combine into words and so on. Ironically, although ASL could have been used to explain sounds related to speech sounds (e.g., how a long vowel differs from a short one), its use was forbidden.

These photographs, taken this century, depict a teacher using a tongue depressor to help manipulate the deaf child's tongue for the position crucial to a particular sound. Also pictured is a typical classroom for deaf students, with children sitting in front of the chart and drawings of the mouth cavity on the blackboard.

Jack Gannon/Deaf Hertiage

An early speech lesson

A typical classroom for deaf students in the early twentieth century

Jack Gannon/Deaf Hertiage

The pure oral method has its roots in Alexander Graham Bell's philanthropic efforts with deaf children during the nineteenth century.[24] Bell, an avowed oralist who promoted pure oralism in the United States, based his efforts on the pathological model. His conflict with the deaf community, over whether or not to include ASL in the education of deaf children, was profound. It appears that Bell's fame, wealth, and influence were too immense for successful resistance from the deaf community.[25] Bell even succeeded in founding an organization based on the pure oral method in 1890–the American Association to Promote the Teaching of Speech to the Deaf. This association was later renamed the Alexander Graham Bell Association for the Deaf, and one of its main goals, to this day, is to disseminate information on pure oral education.

LITERARY QUESTIONS

1) What is ironic about the A. G. Beak Association honoring the principal with a plaque? How do you compare the principal's assurances made to Mama Eagle about Straight Beak's education with the earlier attempts to cure Straight Beak?

2) Do you perceive the beak bending and wing stretching exercises as being potentially successful for the birds? Why do you think that Mama Eagle was easily convinced of the merits of these teaching methods for Straight Beak?

3) Why did the remarks that the birds made about their futures infuriate the teacher? Why is hunting being stressed as the only way of life for the birds?

4) Discuss the analogy between the education of Straight Beak and that of deaf children.

• • •

CHAPTER 4
VOCATIONAL TRAINING

CHAPTER 4		
VOCATIONAL TRAINING		
Topic Unit		
10	11	12
The Flying Lesson	The Hunting Lesson	Evaluation for Graduation
Strophes		
49-53	54-59	60-62

Comprehension Check

Strophc 49

1) T/F- The class is sent to see the principal.

2) What is hoped to be achieved from their vocational training?

Strophe 50

1) T/F- Students sit around the teacher for the lesson.

2) T/F- The teacher requires the students to practice a lot.

3) Y/N- Does the teacher praise students for their first try with the lesson?

Strophe 50 (cont'd)   Time Code

The Signer takes the role of narrator and describes the steps for the flying lessons that Straight Beak and the others need to learn.   11:42.7

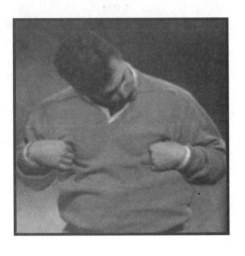

The Signer takes the role of the eagle teacher and gives a demonstration on how to look for prey, with head cocked to the side. The arms depict wings folded.   11:48.1

Strophe 51

1) What does the eagle teacher explain in the first lesson?
   a) that the birds' eyes are set differently
   b) that their heads must turn half-way around
   c) that their eyes must be pointed straight at the target
   d) all of the above

2) T/F- The teacher checks on all of the birds who tried the lesson.

Strophe 51 (cont'd)

Time Code

The eagle's head is set for the hunt.

12:00.3

The lesson outcome is described as pretty good.

12:06.3

Strophe 52

1) T/F- The eagle teacher does a flying demonstration.

2) Y/N- Is there any explanation as to why the birds have difficulty with the flying lesson?

Strophe 53

1) What does the teacher tell the students to do?
   - a) watch for more demonstrations
   - b) keep practicing
   - c) lift their heads higher
   - d) both a and b

2) For the flying lesson, do the birds take turns or go all at once?

3) Y/N- Do the birds go higher and higher in altitude?

Time Code

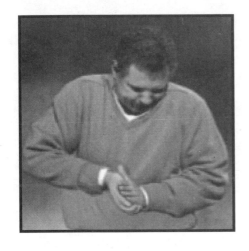

The birds are now described as "extremely competent" flyers.

12:32.7

Strophe 54

1) What lesson does the eagle teacher have to repeat before introducing a new lesson?

2) Describe the position of the animal that the eagle teacher is targeting.

Strophe 55

1) For the new lesson, what does the eagle teacher do with his wings?

2) What is the eagle teacher's dive compared with metaphorically?

The Signer takes the role of the eagle teacher and indicates that he is diving through air or clouds quickly, head first.

Time Code

12:52.3

Strophe 56

1) T/F- Straight Beak's first dive attempt is scary and hard.

2) T/F- Straight Beak does not succeed at diving, and he has to keep practicing.

Strophe 57

1) When the eagle teacher is preparing to land, what does he do besides putting his claws out?

2) What is the eagle teacher's target?

Time Code

The eagle teacher approaches the ground. The Signer narrates and describes the end of the teacher's dive.

13:04.9

The Signer takes the role of the eagle teacher and prepares for the capture, with legs straightened out and claws opened.

13:11.6

Strophe 58

1) Y/N- Is the prey captured and eaten on the spot?

2) T/F- Straight Beak indicates that he already knows the capture lesson.

Strophe 59

1) Y/N- Is the prey that Straight Beak captures real?

2) How does Straight Beak attempt to carry it off?

Time Code

The situation for Straight Beak becomes "unexpectedly complicated." The Signer takes the role of Straight Beak and tells himself that the rabbit is too heavy.

13:37.5

Strophe 60

1) T/F- The eagle teacher thinks that the performance is great.

2) T/F- The eagle teacher lies to Straight Beak about his performance.

3) What tangible reward do the young birds get from the teacher?

Strophe 60 (cont'd)   Time Code

The Signer, in the eagle teacher's role, makes   13:51.1
an announcement and tells the young birds
that they are ready for something.

Strophe 61

1) Who is shedding tears during the graduation ceremony?

2) T/F- Straight Beak leads the procession carrying the school flag.

The Signer takes the role of the families and   13:58.9
responds to the ceremony.

Strophe 61 (cont'd)

The Signer takes the role of Straight Beak and moves his tassel after getting his diploma.

14:06.7

Strophe 62

1) T/F- The parents do not realize that the young birds still have straight beaks.

2) Does Straight Beak feel inhibited by the events on graduation day?

Three family members approach Straight Beak. The Signer, in the role of Straight Beak, watches as they walk up to him.

14:27.5

Strophe 62 (cont'd)   Time Code

Many photographs are taken. The Signer   14:29.0
takes the role of the family members
snapping pictures of Straight Beak.

Background: Educational Tracking and Deaf Children

During school, Straight Beak received training in hunting. Without achieving any real success, the protagonist was praised for his efforts and able to graduate.

Deaf students were once considered less likely to succeed academically as compared to their hearing counterparts. Vocational training was once a common form of education for deaf adults. In fact, vocational training was first emphasized and put to use with deaf students before it became popular with their hearing counterparts.[26] However, this emphasis on vocational training resulted in a disproportionate number of deaf students in the vocational track.

In addition to the academic and vocational tracks, there existed another track: signing allowed or not allowed in the classroom. When pure oralism became popular in the U.S. in the late nineteenth century, many public residential schools for the deaf made a slow transition from manualism to oralism. The term manualism implies the use of signing and fingerspelling as opposed to oralism, which implies the use of speaking and lipreading. As a result, oral and manual tracking for deaf children became commonplace.[27] Schools used oralism to varying degrees, from predominantly manual (e.g., Ohio School for the Deaf) to predominantly oral (e.g., Pennsylvania School for the Deaf). Thus, in one school, there may have been a single speech class or session during the day that deaf students were required to attend. All other classes might be taught either orally or manually.[28] In an oral class, deaf students were expected to lipread the teacher. To do this, students underwent speech lessons throughout the curriculum. Ironically, the older deaf students were more likely to be taught manually regardless of how oralism prevailed during the earlier years.[29]

Deaf students tracked orally were considered brighter and promoted more academically than those in the manual track. In oral classes, signing was strictly prohibited. There were some schools that went so far as to segregate their "prized" oral students to protect them from the so-called "bad influence" of signing students by placing them in separate buildings. There were also many cases of deaf students who, originally tracked orally, could not succeed and eventually had to be placed in the manual track.

The common explanation for "oral failures" placed blame on their mental condition. They were considered intellectually inferior or retarded. Rarely were their difficulties attributed to the pure oral method itself.[30] The consequences of this thinking were damaging, as oral and manual tracking did not account for either intelligence or academic capability.

In recent years, the pure oral method has declined. The major reason for the decline is the research that has uncovered its flaws and criticized the assumptions involved. A number of studies have pointed out that an early signed language experience (e.g., having deaf parents who could sign at home) resulted in more advanced deaf children who progress more rapidly in school. Equally important is the realization that speech ability is not undermined by the knowledge of a signed language.[31] These studies have encouraged the initiation of the bilingual education movement and an overall reform in the deaf education system to try and meet the needs of deaf children more effectively.

LITERARY QUESTIONS

1) What are the implications of Straight Beak being placed on a vocational track? What would become of Straight Beak if he had stayed on the academic track?

2) Why did the teacher keep praising Straight Beak even though he did not hunt well?

3) Does the attempt by Straight Beak to retrieve the dummy rabbit reflect his competence or the failure of the educational philosophy? Why?

4) Do the graduation ceremony and diploma ensure that the birds are now eagles? How does this philosophy correspond to oralism once prevalent in the education of deaf children?

• • •

CHAPTER 5
OUT IN THE WORLD

CHAPTER 5		
OUT IN THE WORLD		
Topic Unit		
13	14	15
Preparation for Hunting	Finding Prey	Bird's Future Considered
Strophes		
63-64	65-69	70-76

Comprehension Check

Strophe 63

1) After arriving home, what does the Eagle family read?

2) What is the plan for the next day?

Time Code

The Signer takes the role of the hunters and expresses their anticipation for successful hunting. A group from the eagle family goes hunting.

14:46.3

Strophe 64

1) What time does Straight Beak wake up?

2) T/F- Papa Eagle is disappointed with Straight Beak's commitment to the trip.

3) Who goes on the trip?
    a) two brothers and Straight Beak
    b) three brothers and Straight Beak
    c) three brothers, Straight Beak, and their father
    d) two brothers, Straight Beak, and their father

Time Code

The Signer takes the role of narrator and describes the difference in Straight Beak's brothers' appearance. The brother eagles are broad-shouldered.

15:02.8

Strophe 65

1) Y/N- Does Straight Beak decide on his own to join the hunting group?

2) Y/N- Does the hunting trip take place right outside the Eagle Family's home?

Strophe 66

1) Who first spots the prey?

2) T/F- Papa Eagle says that he wants to let the prey go.

Time Code

The Signer narrates and describes how the others in the hunting group leave Straight Beak alone.

15:18.1

The Signer narrates to describe the custom among eagles for whomever first sees the prey to do the catch.

15:19.4

Strophe 67

1) What kind of prey is targeted?

2) When Straight Beak starts to circle, what is the Eagle family's reaction?
        a) They are worried and anxious.
        b) They are all impressed.
        c) They think Straight Beak is showing off.
        d) None of the above.

Strophe 68

1) How many in the hunting group swoop for the prey?

Strophe 69

1) Y/N- Does the prey know of his pending fate?

2) T/F- Straight Beak looks to the hunting group above for a signal.

Time Code

The Signer takes the role of the prey and responds with puzzlement as he is caught by claws on his shoulders.

15:52.1

Strophe 70

1) What is Straight Beak trying to do?
> a) flap his wings harder
> b) pick up the prey
> c) hold onto the prey
> d) all of the above

Strophe 71

1) What does Straight Beak request of the prey?

2) What does the prey give Straight Beak to get rid of him?

Time Code

The Signer takes the role of the prey and looks up and reacts to Straight Beak's request with disdain.

16:07.6

The Signer takes the role of Straight Beak and looks down to the prey and begs the prey to go up with him.

16:09.7

Strophe 72

1) T/F- The prey is able to run away.

2) What does Straight Beak deliver to Papa Eagle?

3) What does Papa Eagle realize about Straight Beak?

Strophe 73

1) T/F- Back at home, Papa Eagle sits and tells Mama Eagle what happened to Straight Beak.

Time Code

The Signer takes the role of the hunting group flying home.   16:32.4

Strophe 73 (cont'd)   Time Code

The Signer takes the role of Papa Eagle as he summons Mama Eagle for a meeting.   16:33.6

Strophe 74

1) Y/N- Does Papa Eagle change the story about Straight Beak for Mama Eagle?

2) T/F- Papa Eagle concludes that Straight Beak would have to be taken care of for the rest of his life.

3) What is Mama Eagle's concern?

The Signer takes the role of Papa Eagle and explains Straight Beak's size in proportion to the prey to Mama Eagle.   16:45.3

Strophe 74 (cont'd)   Time Code

The Signer continues in Papa Eagle's role and   16:48.7
gazes away from Mama Eagle wondering who
will watch over Straight Beak.

The Signer takes the role of Papa Eagle and   17:03.5
replies, "That is the point," to Mama Eagle's
concern over Straight Beak.

Strophe 75

1) T/F- Brother Eagles join the meeting on their own.

2) Y/N- Do Brother Eagles accept the request of Mama and Papa Eagle?

Strophe 75 (cont'd)

Time Code

The Signer takes the role of Mama Eagle discussing their death.

17:12.0

The Signer continues in the role of Mama Eagle and asks Brother Eagles if they are willing to accept the responsibility of taking care of Straight Beak when Mama and Papa Eagle pass on.

17:13.9

Strophe 76

1) What is Straight Beak doing during the meeting?

2) Y/N- Does the future plan for Straight Beak require another meeting?

Strophe 76 (cont'd)   Time Code

Straight Beak knows nothing of what is   17:23.0
going on. The Signer takes the role of
narrator and describes Straight Beak's
involvement in the family affairs.

Background: Post Graduation Results for Deaf Children

After years of anticipation, the eagle parents realize that Straight Beak is not really competent in the skills for which he was trained in school. As a result of this new awareness, the eagle parents become depressed and extremely anxious.

This is not an uncommon situation facing parents of deaf children. The graduating deaf child may not be academically competent. This results in an acute sense of failure on the part of parents.[32] As a consequence, "it is not unusual for parents to re-experience all of the vicissitudes of the original grieving process which had occurred after the diagnosis of deafness at infancy."[33]

Two major variables arguably contribute to the failure of the educational system. First, deaf children lack access to curricular content at grade level. Second, educators generally accept the notion that below grade-level performance is to be expected of deaf children.[34]

The first explanation is language-related. Deaf children are not able to use ASL in the classroom environment, and techniques related to teaching English as a second language are not widely promoted or used. The second explanation lies in the beliefs that educators hold. These attitudes may be a result of the unrealistic and inappropriate goals outlined in the pathological model. Thus, with unfulfilled language needs and low expectations in the classroom, deaf children are not able to achieve their full potential upon graduation and beyond.

Although these situations still exist today, the perception of deaf people's abilities by society has become more positive. Deaf people have known all along that they are able, even though this view has not always been shared by the larger population. Also, deaf people often report that they continue to exceed their own hearing parents' expectations by leading a normal and independent life after school. The deaf community provides a wide range of resources and support that is often overlooked by the outsiders. Furthermore, the Vocational Rehabilitation Administration established by the federal government in the 1960s assists with the employment of deaf people.

Today, a deaf person can get assistance from a Vocational Rehabilitation counselor. This usually occurs in cases like that of Straight Beak, where deaf people have been allowed to graduate from high school without sufficient training or academic background to gain employment. The purpose of rehabilitation is to assist the graduate in obtaining employment. The counselor provides support networks depending on the client's individual needs. Among the different types of support are independent living skills training, vocational counseling, on-the-job training, advanced technical training, and/or academic coursework. Deaf people are also eligible for monthly financial assistance, like Supplementary Security Income from the state and federal governments.

While Vocational Rehabilitation has remedied the situation to an extent, it has serious drawbacks. Money spent for deaf children after they complete school increases costs to society. Regardless of money, the underlying issue remains: many deaf people are short-changed, as their full potential remains undermined by their poor education.

As a result of their realization, Straight Beak's parents seek assistance from his siblings to ensure that they will care for Straight Beak even after their death. It is not uncommon to find parents who plan for their deaf child's future and solicit help from the hearing siblings in doing so. There are anecdotal incidences of well-to-do parents who, upon preparing a will, set up a trust fund for their deaf child that is to be executed by one of the hearing siblings. Interestingly, hearing siblings are often given the option: to receive their inheritance in a lump sum or to set up a trust fund to be used at their own discretion. The deaf child is usually not afforded the same choice because the parents believe that their child is not capable of handling the fiscal responsibilities. In addition to monetary concerns, hearing siblings may assume additional responsibilities of care, such as finding living accommodations or securing steady employment for their deaf sibling. Often, these arrangements are made without the deaf person's knowledge or input.

LITERARY QUESTIONS

1) What does Straight Beak's pleading with the rabbit tell us about his own awareness of his abilities?

2) Compare the experience that the parents were confronted with during Straight Beak's hunting failure to the difficulties they had in his infancy.

3) What does the parents' request of the three brothers to take care of Straight Beak after their death tell us about Straight Beak's place in the eagle world?

4) What do you know about the development of Straight Beak's identity in Part One of the narrative?

• • •

PART 2
THE VALLEY

CHAPTER 6
THE BIRD WORLD

CHAPTER 6 THE BIRD WORLD		
Topic Unit		
16	17	18
Family Moves to a New Land	Singing in the Valley	Berries in the Valley
Strophes		
77-82	83-90	91-97

Comprehension Check

Strophe 77

1) When Papa Eagle returns home, what does he do?
   a) gather his things together
   b) wave to get the family's attention
   c) pat his children on the head
   d) fly around the house with excitement

2) Is the Eagle family's new home on the same mountain or a different mountain?

3) What is the one feature that causes this new home to be so wonderful?

Time Code

The Signer takes the role of narrator and explains that time has progressed to a point in the near future.

17:34.4

Strophe 77 (cont'd)   Time Code

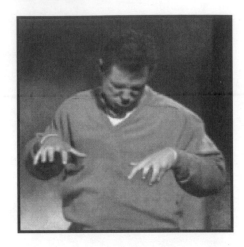

The Signer takes the role of Papa Eagle and tells the audience about the hordes of animals for hunting.   17:45.5

The Signer continues as Papa Eagle telling the audience about the plentifulness of food around their new home.   17:46.7

Strophe 78

1) When does Papa Eagle tell the family they will be moving?

2) Where does the Eagle family put their things?
       a) their suitcases
       b) the family trunk
       c) the car
       d) a moving truck

Strophe 78 (cont'd)   Time Code

The Signer takes the role of family members indicating that they are packing for a long time.

17:52.2

Strophe 79

1) Who is in the lead on the flight to the Eagle family's new home?

2) Y/N- Is Straight Beak able to fly faster and catch up with the family?

The Signer takes the role of the narrator and describes the comparison between Papa Eagle's and Straight Beak's flying speed.

18:13.4

Strophe 80

1) T/F- Straight Beak starts to lose his breath.

2) Y/N- Is Straight Beak able to get his family's attention?

Time Code

Straight Beak is worn out. The Signer explains how Straight Beak feels in trying to keep up with the family.

18:27.5

The Signer takes the role of Straight Beak and modifies one sign to indicate that his scream is muffled.

18:29.8

Strophe 81

1) Why does Straight Beak want to stop?

2) What is Straight Beak's dilemma?

3) From whom specifically does Straight Beak learn about the valley?

Strophe 82

1) Y/N- Does Straight Beak consider other choices besides going down into the valley?

2) Y/N- Does the Eagle family come back to rescue him?

Time Code

18:53.6

Straight Beak decides to proceed with flying downward. The Signer describes his decision to "go ahead."

Strophe 83

1) T/F- Straight Beak almost misses landing on the tree.

Time Code

The Signer, as Straight Beak, expresses relief at finding a tree to land.   19:00.9

The Signer takes the role of Straight Beak who is breathing hard. The sign incorporates the difficulty of the breathing.   19:05.6

Strophe 84

1) What does Straight Beak hear?

2) Where is the bird located?
   a) on the bush next to Straight Beak's
   b) a few bushes over
   c) on a branch on the other side of the tree
   d) on the ground

Strophe 84 (cont'd)

The Signer takes the role of Straight Beak pondering about what he experienced.

19:12.5

Strophe 85

1) Y/N- Does Straight Beak try to avoid staring at the singing bird?

2) What is Straight Beak's comment about the singing bird?

3) T/F- The singing bird believes what Straight Beak tells him.

The Signer takes the role of Straight Beak and has a disgusted reaction to the singing bird.

19:27.7

Strophe 85 (cont'd)   Time Code

The Signer takes the role of the singing bird   19:36.3
and questions Straight Beak about his staring
behavior.

Strophe 86

1) Who gave Straight Beak the information that he shares with the singing bird?

2) What exactly does Straight Beak think?
        a) straight-beaked birds are all well-meaning, but dumb
        b) straight-beaked birds do not exist
        c) straight-beaked birds are all inferior
        d) none of the above

3) What causes the singing bird to laugh?

The Signer takes the role of the singing bird   20:01.5
laughing at Straight Beak's remark.

Strophe 87

1) Y/N- Does Straight Beak move closer to the singing bird during the conversation?

2) What does the singing bird say to Straight Beak?

3) Does Straight Beak say that he could not sing or that he would not sing?

Strophe 88

1) T/F- The singing bird asks another bird to do a demonstration.

2) T/F- Straight Beak has a reaction to his own singing ability.

Time Code

The Signer takes the role of Straight Beak willing to see what his singing ability is like.

20:22.5

Strophe 89

1) T/F- The singing bird repeats the demonstration for Straight Beak.

2) T/F- The singing bird becomes completely involved in the demonstration.

Strophe 89 (cont'd)   Time Code

Straight Beak is mesmerized by the singing.   20:27.0
The Signer describes the character's
involvement.

Strophe 90

1) T/F- Straight Beak describes singing as his first means of truly expressing himself.

2) Y/N- Is Straight Beak afraid of getting too involved in singing?

The Signer takes the role of Straight Beak   20:44.9
and describes his suppressed ability to sing.

Strophe 91

1) How does Straight Beak feel toward the singing bird now?

2) Y/N- The singing bird thinks that Straight Beak's singing is good.

3) What does he want to do for the singing bird to thank him for showing him that he could sing?
        a) find food for the singing bird
        b) demonstrate his diving stunt
        c) sing more for the singing bird
        d) none of the above

4) T/F- The singing bird reacts negatively to the offer.

Strophe 92

1) How does Straight Beak capture the squirrel?

2) T/F- Straight Beak tells the squirrel that he will be eaten.

Strophe 93

1) How does the squirrel get rid of Straight Beak?
        a) by pulling out some of his feathers
        b) by hitting him with a karate chop
        c) by kicking him judo-style
        d) by biting him and screaming

2) T/F- Straight Beak chases the squirrel after he escapes.

Strophe 94

1) T/F- The singing bird questions Straight Beak for wanting to eat the squirrel.

2) What does the singing bird like to eat?

3) T/F- Straight Beak believes that the singing bird's eating habits are inferior.

Time Code

The Signer takes the role of Straight Beak and asks the singing bird if the food is delicious.

21:48.8

Strophe 95

1) Why do both Straight Beak and the singing bird jump down from the tree?

The Signer takes the role of Straight Beak and gulps down the food.

22:02.9

Strophe 96

1) T/F- Straight Beak starts to have indigestion.

2) Y/N- Does the singing bird try to slow down Straight Beak's eating?

Strophe 97

1) What "world" is Straight Beak drawn into?

Time Code

The Signer takes the role of Straight Beak meeting many birds. The sign is modified to show a large number of birds.

22:24.2

The Signer continues in Straight Beak's role and experiences joy in the company of the other birds, which is new to him.

22:28.8

Background: The Acculturation Process and Deaf Children

In this chapter, Straight Beak flies into the valley. This marks his entrance into the bird world. This journey, though not planned, leads the protagonist first into self-denial and then into self-discovery.

This parallels the acculturation process for a large number of deaf people, especially those born to hearing parents. Acculturation is defined as the process of becoming adapted to a new or different culture. There are over one-half million deaf people in the United States, and approximately ninety percent have hearing parents who are not affiliated with the deaf community.[35] Thus a vast majority of deaf children grow up needing to acculturate to deaf culture outside their families since their family members are not a part of the culture.

One common mechanism of acculturation involves residential schools for the deaf. More specifically, the dormitory setting provides deaf children with a rich environment, and the actual socialization process for these children begins when they enroll in school at the age 5 or 6.[36] There are usually one or two residential schools for the deaf in each state, and these deaf children are concentrated in large numbers to achieve effective social experiences. These children rely heavily on one another for emotional support and information about the world.[37] Acculturation is accelerated as certain knowledge, beliefs, and practices that comprise deaf culture are transmitted from child to child.[38] For example, the awareness of ASL and its significance as a fully accessible language via the visual mode is one type of knowledge and belief held by those in the deaf community. The use of ASL serves as practice in this belief system.

Tragically, as some deaf children grow up, they remain stigmatized outside the dormitory as they fail to conform to classroom and society (e.g., to speak instead of signing). This type of stigma reinforces deaf children's identity as different. As a result of these sociocultural processes, the impact of deafness and ASL have been compared to ethnicity.[39]

Some deaf children begin the acculturation process as late as adolescence. They may not begin until after graduation from a public school or private oral school where no signing model was available.[40] Some deaf people never have the opportunity to acculturate into the deaf community. However, with an increase in awareness and willingness to participate in facilitating the acculturation process for deaf children, the hearing parents can provide much-needed support to all ages.

In Straight Beak's situation, he is only able to learn how to sing and eat berries after his formal school years. In the case of late-acculturating deaf adults, often they need to abandon their previous schooling beliefs related to ASL and deaf culture. Learning ASL is a significant move for many deaf adults, and they frequently express their wonder at the ease of learning and using a signed language in comparison to obstacles they faced with a spoken language.

LITERARY QUESTIONS

1) What do the following: the valley, singing, and eating berries symbolize in terms of the deaf experience?

2) How do you account for Straight Beak's resistance to participate in the bird world?

3) What does the epiphany, "All along I have been imprisoned" mean to Straight Beak? How can he be set free?

4) What problems do you detect that may prevent Straight Beak from "acculturating" with the rest of the birds? How can problems like these be removed for potential members of the deaf community?

• • •

CHAPTER 7
RETURN TO EAGLE WORLD

Comprehension Check

Strophe 98

1) Is the reaction to Mama Eagle's arrival positive or negative?

2) What do the birds in the valley do?

Strophe 99

1) Y/N- Does Straight Beak try to hide from Mama Eagle?

2) How would you describe Mama Eagle's landing?
         a) She dives in quickly and lands.
         b) She gently hovers in the air for awhile and then decides to land.
         c) She circles in the air, coming to rest on the tree.
         d) She darts at the other birds and scares them off while landing.

Strophe 100

1) T/F- Mama Eagle angrily slaps Straight Beak's face with her wing.

2) What does the Mama Eagle do after realizing that Straight Beak is missing?
        a) called the police
        b) worried
        c) searched all over for him
        d) b and c

3) T/F- Mama Eagle flies off with Straight Beak.

Time Code

The Signer takes the role of Mama Eagle and expresses frustration over flying back and forth looking for Straight Beak.

22:52.7

The Signer takes the role of Mama Eagle and uses a sign to express contempt.

22:54.3

Strophe 101

1) Y/N- Does Mama or Papa Eagle hit Straight Beak before sending him to his room?

2) Why does the Eagle family gather together?

The Signer takes the role of the narrator. After being brought home, Straight Beak is punished.

22:59.0

Strophe 102

1) Why does Papa Eagle stand up and walk to Straight Beak's room?

2) T/F- Straight Beak is lying on the bed.

3) What is the one word that Papa Eagle screamed?

Strophe 102 (cont'd)

The Signer takes the role of narrator. Straight Beak is singing to himself.

23:16.7

Strophe 103

1) What reason does Papa Eagle give for his anger?

2) What does Papa Eagle threaten to do if he ever catches Straight Beak singing again?

3) Y/N- Is Straight Beak told to leave the room and go outside?

Strophe 104

1) How often does Straight Beak think about his old friends whom he misses?

2) What causes Straight Beak's memories of his old friends to fade?

Background: Realities of Deafness

In this chapter, the eagle parents become upset when they find out that Straight Beak has been acculturated, to some degree, into behaving like a bird. Straight Beak increasingly upholds the values of the bird world and has started to internalize them. Similarly, it is not uncommon for hearing parents with deaf children to become upset when their child begins acculturation into the deaf community. Learning to sign through contact with deaf peers fluent in ASL (primarily deaf children of deaf parents) is part of the acculturation process which might alarm hearing parents. Their signing child is clearly "different." Moreover, their frustration may mount when the deaf adolescent becomes fluent in ASL but is unable to communicate with his hearing parents. The hearing parents' experiences with their deaf adolescents has been described as follows:

> There is a well-known communication gap between parents and adolescents, but...with deaf adolescents this can amount to a chasm. It's a very painful, shocking and sad experience for parents to realize that the child they nurtured is becoming...a virtual stranger in the house...lack of communication skills and apprehension increased the difficulty experienced by parents who tried to answer the adolescent question: "Why am I deaf?" Parents also discussed their concerns about letting go, some dreading the adolescent's separation from the family, particularly if they felt their youngster might choose the deaf world.[41]

In the eagle family, Straight Beak indicated his readiness to join the bird world, but his parents took him home, prolonging their denial of the inevitable. Similarly, there is anecdotal evidence of deaf children who, having completed school and becoming acculturated, are ready to become members of the deaf community, but who are denied this opportunity by their hearing family members. In extreme cases, deaf people were sometimes confined to remaining with their hearing family members in an isolated community like a farm.

In many cases, however, hearing parents finally realize the inevitable. They may regret that they did not learn ASL to help prepare their deaf child more effectively for entry into the deaf world. It seems that the wider community–the hearing world majority–has not recognized or promoted the existence of the smaller deaf community. The deaf adolescent's acculturation finally forces hearing parents to acknowledge the deaf community. The impact of this realization is profound as "there are no more fantasies, no more pretenses, and no magic."[42]

For the benefit of all, parents must overcome misperceptions and work with their deaf child for the benefit of the family:

> As deaf children move closer to adulthood, it becomes more apparent that their acceptance in the wider community is important for their continued or increased happiness. Acceptance of deafness and an understanding of the potential contributions of deaf people to their community is a goal toward which parents, educators, and deaf people themselves continue to work. The increasing visibility of sign language, the increasing availability of sign language interpreters, and the

growing interest in and respect for the deaf community are positive signs that deaf children and deaf adolescents will have the opportunity to take their place as adults in the larger community. The goal of broad acceptance, of alternatives for adults functioning, of a range of options in all areas, is the aim of socialization by parents of all children, not just for those who are deaf.[43]

LITERARY QUESTIONS

1) What does the return to the eagle world imply for Straight Beak?

2) Compare the reaction between Straight Beak and the other birds towards Mama Eagle's landing. Why do you think their responses are different?

3) Has Straight Beak gained any self-identity from his stay in the bird world? Give evidence from this chapter to support your answer.

4) How do you account for Papa Eagle insisting that Straight Beak behave like an eagle, when Straight Beak has failed to acquire "eagle-like" behavior?

• • •

CHAPTER 8
THE OPERATION

CHAPTER 8		
THE OPERATION		
Topic Unit		
21 The News	22 The Cure	23 The Eagle Feast
Strophes		
105-107	108-111	112-114

Comprehension Check

Strophe 105

1) To whom do the parents break the news about Straight Beak?

2) What is the good news?
   - a) they chose a hospital for Straight Beak
   - b) they found a new medicine to try on Straight Beak
   - c) they chose a nurse who would treat Straight Beak for a lower cost
   - d) none of the above

Strophe 106

1) T/F- Surgery is to turn Straight Beak into a normal eagle.

2) What is Straight Beak's reaction?

Strophe 106 (cont'd)

The Signer takes the role of the family members. Everyone in the family encourages Straight Beak to undergo surgery.

24:31.5

Strophe 107

1) What question does Straight Beak pose to his parents?
   a) "Don't you think I look normal now?"
   b) "Will surgery make me normal?"
   c) "Will surgery make me abnormal?"
   d) None of the above.

2) Y/N- Does Straight Beak approve the surgery?

The Signer takes the role of Straight Beak and comtemplates the surgery.

24:34.6

Strophe 108

1) Y/N- Do the parents take Straight Beak to the hospital immediately?

Time Code

The Signer takes the role of narrator and describes Straight Beak while lying on a gurney.

24:49.6

The Signer continues in the role of Straight Beak and responds to the surroundings as he is moved through a corridor.

24:51.5

Strophe 109

1) What kind of room does Straight Beak go into?

2) What is put on Straight Beak's face?

3) T/F- Straight Beak was kissed by his parents.

Strophe 109 (cont'd)   Time Code

The Signer takes the role of Straight Beak and   24:54.3
looks up at the light fixture suspended above.

Strophe 110

1) T/F- Straight Beak's nose is made round by mistake.

2) What is the family's reaction?
> a) They are all very upset.
> b) They just stand there.
> c) They are emotional and crying.
> d) They are depressed and crying.

3) What does the doctor do after walking into the room?

Strophe 111

1) Who reacts first to Straight Beak's new look?

2) How does Straight Beak know what his beak looks like?
> a) The parents show him a picture of it.
> b) The doctor shows him a picture of it.
> c) He sees it in a mirror.
> d) He does not know what his beak looks like; he only sees the family's reaction.

3) What does Mama Eagle proclaim Straight Beak to be?

Strophe 112

1) What is the special occasion for Straight Beak?

2) T/F- Straight Beak's new look is complimented.

Time Code

The Signer takes the role of the onlookers and appears awed by Straight Beak's change of appearance.

25:42.6

Everyone is talking about Straight Beak. The sign indicates that such talking occurs from one person to another.

25:47.6

Strophe 113

1) T/F- Some staring children conclude that Straight Beak looks like a parakeet.

2) Who consoles Straight Beak and what do they say?
       a) A guest: "Don't worry, you'll grow into it."
       b) Papa Eagle: "Before you know it, you'll forget all about it."
       c) The grandmother: "When you get as old as me, you'll never know the difference."
       d) Mama Eagle: "They are just children. They don't know."

3) How does Straight Beak react to the mocking?

Time Code

The Signer narrates to describe the children's reaction to Straight Beak's change in appearance.

26:00.2

The Signer takes the role of Mama Eagle and sends the children away.

26:06.9

Strophe 114

1) What kind of food is at the party?
        a) dirty foods like dirt stew and apple bark pie
        b) a cooked pig with his feet in the air and an apple in his mouth
        c) all kinds of colorful foods
        d) sloppy Joe's and apple pie

2) What other food does Straight Beak want?

3) What excuse does Straight Beak make to get out of eating the food at the party?

Time Code

The Signer takes the role of Straight Beak and tells himself about the food. The sign refers to Straight Beak's dislike of the food.

26:19.8

The Signer in the role of Straight Beak talks to himself regarding his previous experience of eating berries. The sign refers to Straight Beak's spoiled appetite for eagle food.

26:21.0

105

Background: The Cochlear Implant Controversy

In this chapter, Straight Beak consented to his family's wish to have beak-bending surgery. This event is especially relevant, since the protagonist is now an adult and making his own decisions. Recall that the eagle parents considered the surgery option when Straight Beak was a very young eaglet, although they could not afford it.

In the case of deaf children, one controversial type of surgery initiated by parents involves an invasive surgical procedure and the use of cochlear implants. Basically, cochlear implants are electronic prostheses that are inserted in the cochlea to partially replace its function. The implant transduces sound into electrical signals and delivers them to certain parts of the cochlea, bringing direct stimulation to the area where hearing aids fail.

Recall in the narrative that Straight Beak was able to give his consent for the beak-bending surgery. Young deaf children, however, are not able to give consent for the cochlear implant surgery. Routinely, it is a decision made by medical professionals and parents. However, parents may not always be completely informed prior to their decision making.[44] They lack information pertaining to deaf culture and are ignorant of other options, such as learning ASL. Their lack of information makes them vulnerable.

In the 1980s, the United States Food and Drug Administration (FDA) approved the cochlear implant procedure first for adults and later for children. One concern is the experimental nature of the cochlear implants. FDA approval of the implants has been criticized as follows:

> "(c)ochlear implants are highly experimental devices of questionable therapeutic value for most deaf children. On scientific grounds, the FDA should never have given approval for these devices to be taken out of the investigation stage and marketed at will for early-deafened children."[45]

Cochlear implants also have risks. They can sever facial nerves, and they do not fully restore hearing. As a matter of fact, they are primarily effective for deaf people who lost their hearing later in life.[46]

Finally, the social implications for a deaf recipient of cochlear implants have not yet been seriously considered. For example, the device is far more visible than a hearing aid. Both trauma and stress are associated with surgery.

The following New York Times article covers the argument against cochlear implants lying in their representation of the pathological view. The motivation behind the development of cochlear implants is pathological in nature—it is just one approach in the long list of various attempts at "curing deafness."

Pride in a Soundless World:
Deaf Oppose a Hearing Aid

By FELICITY BARRINGER
Special to The New York Times

WASHINGTON, May 15 — Among the rich idioms of American Sign Language, there is a sign for "hearing" — the right index finger, held parallel to the mouth, circling forward like a rolling log. From it comes a second, related sign for a deaf person who thinks like a hearing person: the same finger, circling forward in front of the forehead. It is not a compliment.

A generation after the language and values of deaf people began to win recognition and respect in the hearing world, things "hearing" have acquired a strong stigma at centers of deaf culture. Nowhere is this pride and prejudice more poignant than in the bitter debate over deaf children and a medical device offering them a limited ability to hear.

Kindness or Cruelty?

For doctors and parents--about 90 percent of the quarter-million people who were born deaf or became deaf in early childhood have hearing parents--these recently approved inner-ear implants, known as cochlear implants, offer their children a window on the world of sound. But leading advocates for the deaf say it is brutal to open a child's skull and wind wires through the inner ear, or cochlea, just to rob that child of a birth-right of silence.

In its formal statement on cochlear implants, the National Association of the Deaf deplores "invasive surgery on defenseless children, when the long-term physical, emotional and social effects on children from this irreversible procedure - which will

alter the lives of these children - have not been scientifically established." A cartoon in Silent News, a newspaper for the deaf published in Rochester, shows a gleeful doctor and inane parents grinning down at Dr. Frankenstein's monster.

"From the point-of view of the deaf person, I can quite agree and sympathize that their culture and their language are as acceptable as anyone else's," said Dr. Charles Berlin, an expert on the inner ear and cochlear implants at the Kresge Hearing Research Laboratory at Louisiana State University in New Orleans.

"But nobody can make me say

that a pathological cochlea is acceptable and should be allowed to continue to exist as long as I can do something about it," he said. "I am dedicated to curing deafness. That puts me on a collision course with those who are culturally deaf. That is interpreted as genocide of the deaf."

A spokeswoman for the company that makes the implants, Cochlear Corporation of Englewood, Colo., said 2,630 people in the United States and Canada had received implants since the first trials a decade ago. Usually, the operation costs $25,000 to $35,000.

COCHLEAR IMPLANT:
BEFORE + AFTER...

BEFORE

AFTER

HAPPY DEAF CHILD, NORMAL ASL USING MEMBER OF DEAF COMMUNITY.

UNHAPPY CHILD, <u>FORCED</u> INTO YEARS OF INTENSIVE SPEECH THERAPY TO <u>TRY</u> TO FIT IN A "HEARING WORLD" WITH <u>NO CHANCE</u> OF BEING <u>NORMAL</u> AND <u>SCARRED FOR LIFE</u>.

HANSON
© SILENT NEWS
2/92

A cartoon from Silent News, a newspaper for the deaf based in Rochester, showing one attitude towards the hearing world.

Deaf Say Hearing Aid Collides With Their Culture

After the incision heals, surgeons wind a wire in the patient's inner ear and place a miniature receiver under the skin behind the ear. The apparatus is completed a month later with a miniature computer that detects sound. The computer, which can be worn on the belt, sends electrical signals to the implanted receiver, which then stimulates the auditory nerve, creating sound. How the sound is interpreted, whether as noise or as words, seems to depend on how young the person was when the implant was received, how long the person has been deaf and whether the recipient knew speech before becoming deaf.

Described as Safety Aid

To a doctor like Mary Joe Osberger, director of research in the Department of Otolaryngology at Indiana University School of Medicine, the implant, in most cases, is a safety feature. "We have compelling data to suggest auditory input improves visual attention," she said.

To an educator and linguist like Scott Liddell, who is hearing but has spent a career working among the deaf at Gallaudet University here, the implant is another misguided effort to help deaf children learn a language--the spoken word--that will never really be their own.

Dr. Liddell, chairman of the university's department of linguistics and interpreting, said the typical deaf child can only acquire "some English—and that very late."

Emphasis on English, he said, comes at the expense of early immersion in the visual pageantry of silent life and language. American Sign Language, he said, "is the only language deaf children can acquire on a normal schedule."

In a more general illustration of deaf culture's attitude toward the hearing world, a cartoonist for Silent News, Bruce Hanson, shows a jackboot labeled "Hearing" crushing small figures labeled "Deaf."

Osmond Crosby, a McLean, Va., scientist whose 6-year-old daughter Dorothy Jane, is congenitally deaf and whose 3-year-old daughter, Carina, has a significant hearing loss, angrily brandished the cartoon in a recent interview at his home. "There's only one place for me in that cartoon," he said. "As an oppressor. That's unfair. That's wrong. That makes me mad."

Janet Micari, the mother of Jason, a 9-year-old North Virginia boy who is deaf, said in an interview: "The deaf community has to realize that we are a part of it. You'd better believe I'm a part of it. I consider my child deaf. But I consider him part of my community."

Meeting Half Way

Jason Micari, deafened by meningitis in infancy, took part in one of the earliest tests of the cochlear implant, before the Food and Drug Administration approved it for use in children in June 1990. His mother said he was doing well in public school, where he is taking special classes for the deaf. Another early implant patient, Louis Weiss, a 14-year-old deafened by disease, is an honor student at Earle B.Wood Middle School in Rockville, Md.

Pride in a soundless world, and fierce protection of it.

Tom Willard, editor of "Silent News," stressed the wide variety of viewpoints about those who hear among those who don't, saying, "I've got one foot in the deaf world and one foot in the hearing world."

Hearing parents, he said, can have a place in deaf culture if they "learn sign language and a basic understanding of deaf culture."

"I think it is wrong for a hearing parent to deny a deaf child their cultural identity and force them to be hearing," added Mr. Willard, who lost his hearing as a teen-ager. "Everyone should try and meet in the middle."

Many hearing parents are immersed in deaf culture. "I'm the parent of a deaf child," said Krista Walker, an assistant to Rosalind Rosen, president of the National Association of the Deaf. "I've been to conferences 'on who owns the deaf child.' It's natural to want your child to be part of your community. The irony with deaf children is they will be part of another culture. You cannot identify with concept of deafness if you still have hearing."

Deafness itself eludes precise definition, said Dr. Thomas E. Allen, director of the Gallaudet Center for Assessment and Demographic Studies. "It's not like blindness, with a nice legal definition," he said. Surveys by the National Center for Health Statistics indicate that 21 million Americans have some hearing loss. Extrapolating from the self-reported figures, given in 1990-91, the Government estimates that 450,000 were deaf in both ears; about 250,000 were since birth.

The Deaf Grow Strong

Enrollment in the nation's 60 residential schools for the deaf, which are viewed as important incubators of deaf culture, has been declining, educators at Gallaudet say. The drop reflects the lower birth rates of the late 1970s and early 1980s, the successful efforts to control rubella, which can cause deafness in a fetus, and the mainstreaming movement bringing handicapped children into regular classroom.

CHAPTER 8 THE OPERATION

But American Sign Language has flourished. After the Mark Medoff play and movie "Children of a Lesser God" gave the hearing world a sense of the anger that deaf people can feel at their treatment, hearing entertainers and educators reached out.

Deaf students at Gallaudet needed no hearing help in 1988. Their protests against having a hearing president are successful, and I. King Jordan became the university's first deaf president since its charter in 1864.

But the most important touchstone of deaf culture seems to be the reverence for American Sign Language. With this has come a disdain for other modes used to help the deaf communicate with the hearing—from "oralism," which includes lip reading and was the dominant teaching tool for generations, to manual representations of English, like signed exact English and cued speech. Cued speech renders English syllabically by using 32 signs, all shown near the face, for most of the phonemes that make up everyday speech.

Louis Weiss, the 14-year-old from the Washington suburbs, is among the minority of deaf children relying on cued speech. When he rides the school bus home, says his mother Judy, other deaf children, using sign language, tease him about his "dumb" kind of speech.

Ostracism of Peers

Cheryl Heppner, director of the Northern Virginia Center for Deaf and Hard of Hearing Persons said: "I know kids can be cruel. It isn't something that only hearing kids have cornered the market on."

But, she said, "if parents choose to raise their children only using cued speech, they are cutting off a great source of information and many, many possibilities for learning."

And, she added, children whose basic mode of communication is cued speech and those with cochlear implants face ostracism in parts of deaf society. "I am often mistaken for a hearing person by deaf people who have never met me," she said. "My signs are very English-oriented, and I speak, so they assume I'm hearing. Even after they find out I'm deaf they will regard me with suspicion."

Mr. Crosby and his wife, Deborah, do not believe a cochlear implant is right for Dorothy Jane, although she hears little more than muffled sound even with powerful hearing aids. They fear damaging her residual hearing. Nor will they consider an implant for Carina.

But the Crosbys are also wary of the militants of deaf culture. When, at a meeting with deaf educators, they heard the plea, "give us your deaf children" to be taught in residential schools, Mrs. Crosby responded tartly: "Fine. Give us all your hearing children." The offer, she said, was declined.

The Crosbys say they want their children to know deaf culture, and to know English. "To me it's about choices," Mrs. Crosby said. "If, at 20, Dorothy Jane wants to turn off her voice, that's fine. I want her to have a choice."

Paul Hosefros/The New York Times

Osmond Crosby and his wife, Deborah, said they do not believe a cochlear implant is right for their daughter Dorothy Jane, second from right, although she hears little more than muffled sound with hearing aids and will not consider an implant for their other daughter, Carina.

LITERARY QUESTIONS

1) What does the parents' support of the operation imply about their acceptance of Straight Beak as an adult?

2) What does the children's mocking of Straight Beak tell us about the difference between children and adults in general? Discuss why adults praise Straight Beak even though he appears more like a parrot than an eagle.

3) What does the parrot symbolize in terms of Straight Beak's involvement in the eagle world?

4) How do you compare Straight Beak's consent to have an operation with that of deaf children undergoing surgery for cochlear implants? Discuss the limitations of cochlear implants and their impact on deaf children.

● ● ●

CHAPTER 9
THE FLIGHT

CHAPTER 9			
THE FLIGHT			
Topic Unit			
24	25	26	27
Return to the Valley	Ejected from the Choir	The Berry Struggle	The Flight into Sunset
Strophes			
115-117	118-121	122-123	124-126

Comprehension Check

Strophe 115

1) When Straight Beak wakes up in the morning, what is he thinking of doing?

2) What is the return deadline that the mother gives Straight Beak?

Time Code

The Signer takes the role of Straight Beak and engages in dialogue with Mama Eagle explaining that he will stay around the area.

26:56.1

111

Strophe 116

1) Y/N- Does Straight Beak try to avoid joining the group of singing birds?

2) Y/N- Do the singing birds stop singing and stare at Straight Beak?

3) What question does the singing bird ask Straight Beak?

Strophe 117

1) What is the reason for Straight Beak to lie about his beak?

2) Y/N- Does Straight Beak say his beak would be fixed?

Time Code

The Signer narrates that Straight Beak is avoiding telling the truth.

27:31.4

112

Strophe 117 (cont'd)

The Signer describes Straight Beak's beak bending as a result of crashing into a window.

27:35.3

Strophe 118

1) Y/N Does the choir persuade Straight Beak to join?

2) What causes the director to stop the singing choir?

3) T/F- The choir director finds one musical instrument that was not working right.

The Signer takes the role of the singing birds and expresses their condolences for Straight Beak's accident.

27:39.1

Strophe 119

1) How does the choir director detect the problem?

2) What is Straight Beak's problem with singing?
        a) His beak is crooked.
        b) His air flow is directed down instead of out.
        c) He does not like the music.
        d) Both a and b.

3) T/F- The choir director becomes disgusted and decides to leave.

Time Code

The Signer narrates the problem occurring in the choir. The sign refers to the distortion of sounds.

27:58.8

Strophe 120

1) T/F- Straight Beak has to sit on a different chair in the choir.

2) What desire does Straight Beak express to the director?
        a) to sing a different song
        b) to direct the choir
        c) to leave the choir
        d) none of the above

Strophe 121

1) How long does Straight Beak sit with the choir?
    a) all afternoon
    b) one hour
    c) all evening
    d) all day

Time Code

The Signer takes the role of Straight Beak and tries to hum without singing while watching the choir.

28:36.3

Strophe 122

1) T/F- One bird is hungry and ready to eat.

2) T/F- All the berries are at the place where the birds are singing.

3) T/F- Straight Beak wants to eat berries.

The Signer narrates Straight Beak's goal for going into the valley.

28:55.3

Strophe 123

1) What color are the berries?

2) What happens to the berries when Straight Beak tries to eat them?

Strophe 124

1) Describe Straight Beak's new approach to eating berries.

2) Y/N- Are the other birds having problems, too?

3) Y/N- Does Straight Beak realize he cannot eat berries anymore?

Time Code

The Signer takes the role of Straight Beak's struggle of trying to eat the berries.

29:26.0

CHAPTER 9 THE FLIGHT

Strophe 125

1) What does Straight Beak see to <u>his</u> right?
   a) the great expanse of the forest
   b) the mountains with eagles circling
   c) different kinds of berries
   d) the valley birds eating, singing, and having a good time.

2) What does Straight Beak see to <u>his</u> left?
   a) the great expanse of the forest
   b) the mountains with eagles circling
   c) different kinds of berries
   d) the valley birds eating, singing, and having a good time.

Strophe 126

1) What does Straight Beak see in front of him?

2) When Straight Beak begins flying, is he hesitant or resolute?

LITERARY QUESTIONS

1) What do the following tell us about Straight Beak's character?
   a) He accepts the idea that he is an "eagle," but he still craves berries.

   b) He thinks the eagle world is superior, but he is anxious to join the choir.

2) In the choice between the bird and the eagle world, how does Straight Beak decide on his fate?

3) How has Straight Beak's identity evolved in Part Two of the narrative?

• • •

For a
Decent Living

*F*or a Decent Living, as told by Sam Supalla, comments on a deaf boy's journey in search of his identity after leaving his hearing family. The narrative focuses on obstacles that the protagonist must overcome in order to make a decent living in a hearing world. The protagonist encounters conflict, dilemma, triumph, and rejection, as the series of unfolding events further develop his character. The impact of this story is profound, as the particular experiences the protagonist faces are shared by many members of the deaf community and other minority groups.[47]

The use of the first-person point of view in *For a Decent Living* is engaging—it helps to draw the viewer into the events and to share in the boy's plight. The Signer is skillful at using the first person to develop a rapport with the audience; this maximizes the audience's understanding of deaf experiences related to identity development.[48] The first chapter of the narrative acts as a prologue, filled with images and symbols that explain the character's background and set up the action that follows.

• • •

CHAPTER 1
LIVING ON THE FARM

CHAPTER 1	
LIVING ON THE FARM	
Topic Unit	
1	2
The Farm Family	Incident in the Barn
Strophes	
1-4	5-9

Comprehension Check

Strophe 1

1) Give a general description of the setting.

2) Identify the general geographic location of the setting.

3) T/F- Snow is falling.

Time Code

The Signer takes the role of narrator. The landscape is described as flat and distant, signed in a way that moves you across the land.

5.5

123

Strophe 1 (cont'd)   Time Code

The Signer continues in the role of narrator   8.0
and describes wind gusts blown into the face.

The Signer, in the role of narrator, describes   8.5
snow accumulating.

Strophe 2

1) T/F- Snow is blowing over the ground.

2) Y/N- Is there a snow drift against the side of the house?

3) What is the boy doing in the house?

Strophe 2 (cont'd)

The house is shown as if a movie camera moves on a dolly around it. The Signer attempts to create a cinematographic effect for the audience.

20.3

The sign for window is shown. The following scene depicts the window as if a movie camera is zooming in to the house through it.

26.5

Strophe 3

1) What comes out of the father's mouth?

2) Y/N- Does the boy respond verbally?

3) Who comes into the room next?

Strophe 3 (cont'd)

The Signer narrates about the father who is staggering and stomping; liquor sways in his glass.

39.6

The Signer takes the role of the father who attempts to make a verbal demand to the boy. The sign depicts the father's slurred speech.

42.8

A sign is used to describe an explosion of verbal fighting taking place.

52.6

Strophe 4

1) Y/N- Is the boy successful in leaving the fight scene?

2) What does he put away before leaving?

3) What clothes does he put on?

Strophe 5

1) T/F- The boy opens the door and enters another room.

2) Why is the boy's scarf flapping in the air?

3) Y/N- Is the boy able to run to the barn quickly?

Time Code

The Signer describes how the boy walks against the wind.

1:32.3

Strophe 6

1) T/F - The boy finds his way easily into the barn because of the light from outside.

2) What situation does the boy find himself in when he enters the barn?

Time Code

Snow is swirling inside the barn as a result of the boy's opening and shutting the barn door.

1:50.1

Strophe 7

1) How does the boy find the lantern?

2) T/F- There is no problem with the lantern when it is being lit.

The Signer describes how the wick is lit.

2:05.8

Strophe 8

1) What is on the ground inside the barn?

2) What animals does the boy find?
        a) cows
        b) pigs
        c) sheep
        d) horses

3) Are there many animals or just a few?

4) What is the boy looking for?

                                                                                 Time Code

The Signer describes how the boy uses the lantern to illuminate the barn floor.   2:12.7

The Signer describes what the boy encounters–animals roaming all around.   2:18.5

129

Strophe 8 (cont'd)   Time Code

The sign refers to a shovel the boy is   2:23.4
looking for.

Strophe 9

1) T/F- The boy breaks the window.

2) What is nailed over the broken window?

3) Why does the boy become angry?

The Signer describes the shattered barn   2:29.7
window.

Background: Language Accessibility

The protagonist is a deaf child of non-signing parents. The quality of this family's interaction is evidently poor; the father's attempts at communicating by speaking not signing results in no response from the protagonist. The boy is unable to participate in an interactive manner or follow the clash between his father and mother. Only a spoken language is used by the parents, and the boy experiences a form of isolation as he lacks needed verbal interaction. Although both parents are supposedly aware that their child is deaf, this does not necessarily mean that they will learn and use ASL.

Lack of signing by both parents and child is plausible, given the historical nature of how ASL was once scorned as a language. The parents may have been advised specifically not to sign, and if this was the case, the events as told are more likely to have occurred prior to the 1970s. It is interesting to note that, regardless of the lack of verbal communication at home for the boy, he still manages to rely on cues and context whenever possible. For example, in the narrative, the boy understood what his father wanted and went to the barn. Although the boy may have routinely cleaned out the barn, on this particular day, as told he had not completed this chore. Thus, from context, it was not surprising that the father became furious and pointed at the barn as he screamed at the boy. In this case, the boy was able to follow what was happening and go to the barn, despite his mother's protest.

Had a different interaction occurred, the chain of events may have unfolded completely differently. In considering certain aspects of the deaf experience, one can imagine how the narrative could change. Had the parents used ASL with the boy, he may have responded verbally to his father and given an explanation as to why he had not completed his chores. Similarly, the chain of events may have been altered had the boy confronted his father verbally instead of running away.

Ironically, although the boy does not sign throughout the entire chapter, this does not mean that he lacks competence in ASL. Considering his relative age, the protagonist is old enough to have enrolled in school. Assuming he attended a residential school for the deaf, he would have been expected to have achieved competence in ASL. Unfortunately, the dominant approach in the education of deaf children at that time was strictly oral, and the boy would not have received the needed support in the classroom, or at home. Thus, even though the boy was able to communicate verbally, conflict still occurred because the parents did not take into consideration the language needs of their son.

LITERARY QUESTIONS

1) How does the mood of the protagonist relate to the description of farmland and the inside of the farmhouse?

2) Describe the behavior of the boy and his father as far as communication is concerned.

3) Is there any symbolic relationship between painting and the protagonist's deafness?

4) If you have a hearing friend or relative who happens to have a deaf child and this person does not know any ASL, would you interfere? Why or why not?

• • •

CHAPTER 2
MOVING TO THE CITY

CHAPTER 2	
MOVING TO THE CITY	
Topic Unit	
3	4
Meeting the Deaf Peddler	Finding the Deaf Club
Strophes	
10-14	15-16

Comprehension Check

Strophe 10

1) T/F- The boy looks up at the skyscrapers.

2) T/F- The boy drops his baggage and stands with two other people.

Time Code

The sign indicates the boy's eventful journey to his destination, the city.

2:54.7

133

Strophe 10 (cont'd)   Time Code

The Signer describes the busy sidewalk with   **3:06.2**
many people passing by.

The Signer takes the role of the boy dropping   **3:09.2**
his suitcases.

Strophe 11

1) What draws the boy to look into the store window?

2) How long does he windowshop?
        a) all day
        b) all afternoon
        c) five hours
        d) none of the above

Strophe 11 (cont'd)

Time Code

A store window is shown as if a movie camera moves on a dolly passing the window.

3:29.5

The Signer takes the role of the boy, windowshopping at a leisurely pace, who is awed by the busy city life.

3:37.4

Strophe 12

1) The boy gets the ABC card by:
   a) picking it up off the ground
   b) asking a man for directions
   c) having it handed to him
   d) b and c

2) T/F- The boy finds that the card is printed with the manual alphabet and a request for money.

3) What does the boy ask the peddler?

Strophe 12 (cont'd)   Time Code

The Signer describes the peddler taking his   4:09.5
card back from the boy.

Strophe 13

1) T/F- The peddler runs away from the boy.

2) T/F- A cop is able to catch and stop the peddler.

The peddler runs through the crowd.   4:12.6

Strophe 13 (cont'd)

The Signer describes the detail and shabbiness of the peddler's coat.

4:20.9

Strophe 14

1) What does the boy ask the peddler?

2) T/F- The peddler helps write down the information.

3) T/F- The boy disappears after getting the needed information.

The Signer takes the role of the peddler and fingerspells a place where there are deaf people.

4:26.5

Strophe 15

1) T/F- The boy stands inside the trolley when it moves.

2) T/F- The trolley stops immediately after it starts moving.

Time Code

The sign depicts the boy boarding and riding the trolley.   4:41.0

The trolley jostles along with a rod attached to a cable above.   4:49.2

Strophe 16

1) T/F- There are three street lights where the boy gets off the trolley.

2) Why does the boy walk under one of the streetlights?

3) Y/N- Does the boy think he found the place from his directions?

Strophe 16 (cont'd)

Time Code

The Signer takes the role of the boy and looks outside before stepping out of the trolley.

4:59.8

The Signer describes the streetlight shining and creating a circle of light on the ground.

5:08.5

Background: The Peddling Controversy

The boy's encounter with a deaf peddler is awkward. Traditionally, deaf peddlers attempt to play on the sympathy of hearing strangers by using their deafness to sell certain items, especially small cards printed with the manual alphabet. Peddling has long been a significant part of the deaf community, tracing back to the 1930s and peaking between World War II and the late 1950s.

Peddling is a stigma in the deaf community. Deaf peddlers would go underground in order to make their living. Ironically, they would do anything to avoid deaf pedestrians, but due to the transparency of deafness, they were not always successful in their hiding.

The controversial peddling issue may not be widely known or important to the general public, but the following *Deaf USA* article by Mr. David Rosenbaum indicates how profound it is in the consciousness of many deaf people. The controversy lies in the image that deaf community leaders attempt to create for the public–an image which peddlers undermine. This concern is not necessarily warranted, and despite objections, peddlers continue their work in bars, restaurants, stores, libraries, and public transportation.[49]

'ABC Peddling': An Overview

DAVID ROSENBAUM
Staff Writer

The term "ABC peddling" in the Deaf community is used to refer to a person or group of people who sell cards or items. They often did this work full-time and usually put the manual alphabet (fingerspelling) on these cards or items.

These peddlers often approach people and show the card or item. There will usually be a message asking for a donation, a contribution or money to buy food or to support a family because of their "handicap."

In the *Gallaudet Encyclopedia of Deaf People and Deafness,* John V. Van Cleve says that deaf peddling in the 1930s was seen as a problem. "Peddling carried the same connotations as begging, that is, deaf people were a helpless and dependent class. Some deaf people played on the sympathy of hearing strangers by using their deafness to sell them overpriced items, especially small cards with the manual alphabet reproduced on them.

"The NAD [National Association of the Deaf] in the 1930s called this kind of selling a 'form of begging' and condemned the practice. Like outright begging, peddling implied that deaf people could not compete in the marketplace and that they should be pitied," Van Cleve adds.

"What a tremendous handicap it is to have organized gangs of the worst specimens, the 'tough looking crews,' brazenly going about the country," Tom L. Anderson, NAD president declared in 1942, "introducing themselves everywhere at front doors as deaf people in need of help, indicating clearly that all they can do to earn a living is to sell worthless trinkets from door to door!"

The Other Side

There is another side, however, to the concept of peddling. Peddling became popular during an era when there were no equal opportunity or legislation protecting the rights of a deaf person in obtaining employment.

In the 1930s, having choices to formal education were less available than they are today. The Social Security Supplemental Income (SSI) program did not start until 1974. The Social Security Disability (SSDI) program which started in 1956 required that the person had worked before he or she became disabled.

There are people who argue for the right of a deaf person to sell manual alphabet (ABC) cards or small giftware items as long as these people have the appropriate licenses and pay all applicable taxes. One person **Deaf USA** spoke with compared it to the veterans of the Vietnam war "peddling" pencils.

In this situation, they argue, which is better for an uneducated deaf person: to apply for and receive SSI benefits, or to get a license to work as a legitimate "peddler" and pay employment taxes? A person who works and pays federal taxes would then be able to go on Social Security when he or she retires.

The Krakovers

Leon Krakover of Chicago, IL, was a printer. Because of his lung problem, he looked for a different job and eventually organized other deaf people to sell products. It was during the 1930s, when jobs were lacking for deaf people. Educational opportunities were also very limited. At that time, there was no such thing as "welfare" or some sort

Hyman Krakover (left) with brother, Leon Krakover (right).

of government subsidy for a deaf person.

His younger brother, Hyman, eventually joined his business. Leon would take care of the business side while Hyman would drive Leon around. Leon would go to deaf people's homes and look for people who needed work. The business was so successful that Leon purchased his first apartment building in 1943. Then, in 1939, Hyman met his future wife, Helen, in Pittsburgh, PA for the first time. They fell in love.

Helen then decided to move to Chicago, IL, to help manage an apartment building for Leon called the Krakover Apartments. The building was located in Humboldt Park, which used to be a prestigious part of Chicago. At one time, Leon owned six buildings.

northern states in the summer," Helen recalls during an exclusive interview with **Deaf USA**. "Leon would even buy brand new cars for each group to travel in. He was a very generous man. They would stay at hotels.

"Everyone who worked would get a percentage of whatever they sold. Each group leader kept records of all income, and a larger percentage, naturally, would go to Lenny [Leon].

"Leon gave his people time off on weekends. They never worked on weekends. They would go and have good times Saturday nights and all day Sundays."

In 1944, Helen and Hyman married. That year, Leon also started paying Social Security and income taxes for his peddlers for the first time.

stores and show a 'tool box' which had needles, screwdrivers and useful gadgets such as key rings. The key ring would also have a piece with edges which could be used as a handy 'screwdriver.' Leon and Hyman would purchase these items from wholesale places."

Helen says that peddling these items were good ways of income for children who were neglected by their parents. With income, they could not only get work, but have money, buy food and find accommodations.

At no time did they visit homes. Leon Krakover even converted the garages in back of two apartment buildings that they owned in Chicago to a clubhouse with a billiard table, counters, chairs and food, including hot dogs. At that time, Helen was working in the rental office and delivering fresh linen in exchange for dirty linen in Leon's buildings. Her rental office was then moved into the clubhouse.

Most of the tenants living in their apartment buildings were hearing people. When hearing people moved out, Leon would sometimes let his peddlers and deaf people rent one of his apartments.

Several Chicago apartment buildings that Leon Krakover owned in the 1940s.

Posing as Deaf Peddlers

The Krakover operation is just one operation. There were many other deaf peddlers. And many hearing people also acted as "deaf" peddlers!

In a newspaper report printed on March 21, 1956, George Peterson reveals that "there are an estimated 4,000 fake deaf mutes panhandling across the United States." Peterson, himself hearing and "one of the most successful street beggars west of Baghdad," according to police, also said that he worked "four hours - playing the deaf mute racket - and my daily quota is $20. Holidays my take gets as high as $100."

At first Leon Krakover did his own selling. Then, when Hyman joined, other people started to work for Leon. Leon, then decided to assign workers that he trusted to lead more groups. Eventually their business became so big that these groups peddled items in all 48 states, according to Helen Krakover.

"These groups would visit each state depending on the season, i.e., they would go to the southern states during winter, and go to the

Concept of Peddling

Leon passed away in Chicago, IL on May 2, 1991 at 87 years old. Following him, Hyman passed away in Los Angeles, CA, in February, 1922, at 85. Helen was most helpful in clarifying the peddling concept.

"They *never* sold manual ABC [alphabet fingerspelling] cards, despite all the misinformation that has been spread around. What they did was they would go only into

The Ontario Association of the Deaf takes a serious view of the activities of these peddlers, in as much as the Association placed upwards of 135 individuals in good jobs at us own expense, many of whom made from $40 to $50 a week. Their activities give the great mass of honest, hard-working deaf a black eye and make it all the harder for them to accrue employment when necessary. Some of these peddlers travel from coast to coast. That costs money, yet they can do it and staying at hotels costs more than the average worker can afford, yet these peddlers can afford that luxury. The O.A.D. knows of cases where much peddlers have graduated into petty embezzlers. The great difficulty in bringing these to book is getting the victims to lay charges.

In this campaign to stamp out these unprincipled individuals, we have the backing of Better Business Bureau and the National Employment Service. We ask that hotel managers deny these persons the privilege of peddling in their beverage rooms, and that municipalities carefully scrutinize their requests for peddling licenses and that the Provincial and Municipal Police check up on individual or gangs of such peddlers as may be operating within their jurisdiction from time to time.

May we have your co-operation ?

THE ONTARIO ASSOCIATION OF THE DEAF

MERRY CHRISTMAS

Hello!

I AM A DEAF MUTE

I am selling this *Deaf Mute Education System* card to make my living.

THANK YOU
(over)

I AM A DEAF MUTE

I AM SELLING THIS CARD TO MAKE A LIVING

PAY ANY PRICE YOU WISH

THANK YOU

HAPPY NEW YEAR!

NFSD: Enraged

In the July, 1941 issue of *The Frat,* a publication of the National Fraternal Society of the Deaf (NFSD) in Chicago, IL, the late Francis P. Gibson, a NFSD official, was said to have entered a bank where he was not known. He presented a written memorandum to a bank official. The official, without reading the memo or looking at Gibson, gave him a quarter. Obviously, "some beggar, impostor or deaf, had been working this bank."

NFSD Court Case

NFSD officials were also very active in distributing printed materials condemning deaf peddlers. In the November 1941 issue of *The Frat,* they point out that this type of beggar does more harm than good. "An employer who does not know anything about the deaf is not likely to have a very high opinion of a deaf applicant for a job, once he has come in contact with a deaf panhandler."

In 1948, Leon Krakover filed two lawsuits: a one million dollars lawsuit against the NFSD and also a $100,000 lawsuit against the Chicago Club of the Deaf. **Deaf USA** contacted past and present NFSD officials who tried to recall details of this court case. Apparently, one of NFSD's printed material was posted on the bulletin board of a local deaf club. In the lawsuit, Krakover claimed that NFSD was "interfering with their business."

In a letter to the New York School for the Deaf in October 1949, A.L. Roberts, the NFSD Grand President, says that "the court cases against the Society (NFSD) and the Chicago Club are still pending and that is all. We have tried three times to bring the cases to trial but the other side stalls. Probably they will continue to stall until the matter is either squashed or thrown out."

In February, 1953, NFSD announced that they countersued Leon Krakover. In their counter-complaint, NFSD requested that the 'Code for the Regulation and Supervision of Itinerant Selling by Deaf Persons' be enforced. "Eventually, the suit was thrown out but it cost us a tidy sum in lawyer fees," according to Frank Sullivan, NFSD past Grand President. "The judge said that he could find no one guilty and suggested that we sit down and see how we could make rules to lessen the bad taste of peddling."

Reprinted with permission, Deaf USA – a national newspaper, ISSN #0898-5480 – Eye Festival Communications, North Hollywood, CA 91607.

LITERARY QUESTIONS

1) With the mood of the city being different from that of the farmland, does the boy feel less isolated? Why?

2) How do you account for the boy's fascination with the shop windows? What do you think the mannequin in the window represents to him?

3) What does the peddler represent for the boy? Do you think the protagonist has a stigmatized image of peddlers?

4) What would you do if you encounter a deaf peddler in the same way as the boy did? Share any experiences you may have had in dealing with peddlers.

• • •

CHAPTER 3
VISITING THE DEAF CLUB

CHAPTER 3		
VISITING THE DEAF CLUB		
Topic Unit		
5	6	7
Meeting the Club Members	The Job Market	Banished from the Deaf Club
Strophes		
17-20	21-25	26-29

Comprehension Check

Strophe 17

1) Y/N- Does the boy find the door of the building locked at first?

2) T/F- The boy had to go downstairs to the basement.

3) When he opens the second door at the end of the hall, what does he see?
   a) a room filled with people signing
   b) a smoke-filled room
   c) a room filled with people talking
   d) a and b

Time Code

The Signer takes the role of the boy as he sticks his head past the corner to look before walking down the hallway.

5:43.2

Strophe 17 (cont'd)

The door is shown as if a movie camera   5:52.0
moves on a dolly towards it. As a result, the
door gets closer and closer.

Strophe 18

1) T/F- The boy approaches the hunchback after he enters the room.

2) What three questions does the hunchback ask the boy?

3) Y/N- Does the hunchback recognize the boy?

The Signer takes the role of the hunchback   6:22.0
and asks the boy about which residential
school for the deaf he attended.

Strophe 19

1) T/F- The boy introduces himself to the club members.

2) T/F- The boy is embarrassed about meeting new friends.

Strophe 20

1) What are the people doing at the table?

2) How does the boy feel about interrupting the club president?
    a) hesitant
    b) eager
    c) upset
    d) won't do it

3) T/F- The club president asks the boy to sit down.

Time Code

The Signer takes the role of the hunchback holding the boy's arm and pushes him forward to the table.

6:49.0

Strophe 20 (cont'd)

The table is shown as if a movie camera moves on a dolly towards it. As a result, the table appears bigger and bigger.

6:52.7

The Signer describes the club members getting up and leaving the table.

7:14.7

Strophe 21

1) What is the boy's answer to the question of why he came to the club?

2) Why does the club president say "you are lucky"?
      a) because he knows the hunchback
      b) because the hearing men went to war in Germany and Japan
      c) many factory jobs were open
      d) both b and c

3) What does the boy ask at the end?

Strophe 21 (cont'd)

Time Code

The Signer describes how hordes of men have entered the war.

7:49.6

The Signer describes how the factories are in need of workers during the war.

7:51.9

Strophe 22

1) T/F- The club president summons two workers by name signs.

2) How are these workers ranked in their roles in the deaf community?

Strophe 22 (cont'd)   Time Code

The club members tap shoulders until they reach the right person for the club president.   8:05.1

Strophe 23

1) T/F- The boy asks the printer to tell about the printing job prospect.

2) Write down the abbreviation that the printer spells out.

3) What does he say about a job opening?

The Signer takes the role of the printer and explains about his job being highly paid.   8:33.8

Strophe 24

1) What does the sawmill worker say about the job opportunities at this time?
   - a) It was too early to tell.
   - b) There were job openings at the sawmill.
   - c) The jobs were all taken.
   - d) That only recently had they considered hiring deaf people.

2) What does the sawmill worker have on his face?

3) What is the boy horrified about?

Time Code

The Signer takes the role of the sawmill worker and identifies his occupation. The sign for sawmill is commonly used in the Pacific Northwest.

8:49.0

Strophe 25

1) How does the boy respond to the job at the aircraft factory?
   - a) He is enthralled because of his childhood fascination with planes.
   - b) He is excited because his father and grandfather had worked in aircraft factories as well.
   - c) He is excited because the club president worked for the factory, too.
   - d) Both a and b.

2) T/F- The aircraft factory is small.

3) What does the club president say about deaf people working at the factory?

Strophe 26

1) Who does the boy see behind the club president?

2) How exactly does the club president respond?
        a) He gets angry and pounds his gavel on the table.
        b) He throws his cards on the table.
        c) He becomes furious and bangs his fist on the table.
        d) He angrily swears in sign.

Time Code

The Signer describes the cards scattering as a result of the club president's banging on the table.

9:49.4

Strophe 27

1) T/F- The club president stands up angrily in front of the boy.

2) What causes the club president to accuse the boy of being a peddler?

3) Why is the boy considered a liar?

Strophe 27 (cont'd)

Time Code

Both the printer and sawmill worker look at the boy in dismay.

9:59.2

The Signer takes the role of an "unnamed" club member taken by surprise with the club president's anger and signs, "What?"

10:11.0

Strophe 28

1) Who comes to the boy's rescue?

2) Y/N- Does the club president say, "Stay here!"?

3) T/F- Only the boy leaves the clubroom.

Strophe 28 (cont'd)   Time Code

All of the club members looked down at the   10:24.6
boy as he left the clubroom.

The Signer takes the role of the boy getting   10:27.6
the door slammed in his face.

Strophe 29

1) Where does the boy stop?
   a) at the end of the hall
   b) outside the building
   c) at the top of the stairs
   d) none of the above

2) What does the hunchback offer the boy?

Strophe 29 (cont'd)

Time Code

The Signer takes the role of the boy and denies his involvement with peddling.

10:36.1

The Signer takes the role of the boy and reluctantly leaves the club with the hunchback.

10.46.3

Background: Deaf Club as a Haven

The protagonist was drawn to finding the deaf club in the hopes of finding a haven in a large and unfamiliar city. This perception of the deaf club as a haven is universal among deaf people. Although he was able to locate the deaf club, he was later ejected from it. This rejection is profound, as the protagonist was shunned by his own people.

There is usually at least one deaf club in each large city in the United States. The Union League of the Deaf was the first deaf club established in the United States in 1886 in New York City. It was followed by hundreds throughout the next century.[50] Philadelphia used to have two deaf clubs, but the number has since gone to one. Metro-Boston still has three of its own.

The setting, organization, and function of deaf clubs are rather uniform nationwide. In the narrative, the deaf club portrays a familiar setting. For example, one could describe the Typical Club of the Deaf (TCD) by first how members or visitors enter the building:

> ...we must climb a steep staircase. At the top of the stairs, we turn into a long, narrow room, furnished in a style we might call 'early Goodwill.' Tables covered with oilcloth tacked to their tops are surrounded by plain wooden chairs and, against one wall, sits a worn sofa that has probably been donated. Across the room from the entrance is a bar, the money spent at the bar pays TCD's rent. Next to the bar stands a television set. At the far end of the room is a small platform. It serves as the stage for lectures, plays, or other entertainment." [51]

The role of deaf clubs is further described in a well-received play, *Tales of a Clubroom* by Bernard Bragg and Eugene Bergman. According to the 1981 script, deaf people laughed at the events which reflected "...the vibrant and buoyant life of a close-knit community." (p. xii).

> In any city, the club of the deaf is the heart of the deaf community. It is the principal meeting place and forum of the deaf. It is, in most cases, the only place where they can socialize. It is their ballroom, their bar, their motion picture house, their theater, their coffeehouse, their community center–all rolled into one. It is a piece of their own land in exile–an oasis in the world of sound.

Not only for social purposes, deaf clubs are expected to keep people abreast of job opportunities. For example, the protagonist learns about certain job opportunities at the club. In his case, the club provides the needed networking among its deaf members for employment in the hearing world.

According to the documentary film, *The Los Angeles Club of the Deaf Story,* entire buildings can be owned by clubs. The revenue from renting the unused space provides support for the club activities. Unfortunately, as documented in the film, the Los Angeles club has suffered a drastic drop in membership leading to its closure, and the same holds true for a number of other clubs across the country. The Los Angeles club reached its zenith during World War II and the following years, but the lifestyle of its members has since changed dramatically. One such change is the introduction of teletypewriter devices, which allow deaf people to make contacts among themselves more efficiently. The invention of these devices enable deaf people to make plans for socialization without having to go to a club.

LITERARY QUESTIONS

1) Describe and contrast the setting and atmosphere of the hallway and clubroom.

2) Discuss the particular questions that the doorman asked the boy. What purpose do you think these questions serve the doorman and the deaf club at large?

3) What does the boy's reaction to the people with power in the club tell us about his character? Describe the image created for the club president based on his physical description and the way he presented himself to the boy.

4) How do you explain the paradox of the club president kicking the boy out of the deaf club but permitting the peddler to stay?

• • •

CHAPTER 4
GETTING A JOB

CHAPTER 4				
GETTING A JOB				
Topic Unit				
8 The Aircraft Factory	9 The Job Request	10 A Job Found	11 In the Factory	12 The Good Worker
Strophes				
30-31	32-37	38-40	41-44	45-47

Comprehension Check

Strophe 30

1) T/F- The boy sleeps well through the night.

2) What does he resolve to do?

3) What transportation does the boy use to leave the place where he slept?

Time Code

The Signer takes the role of the boy and thinks to himself about what he should do from then on.

10:59.0

Strophe 30 (cont'd)   Time Code

It is early in the morning when the boy makes his resolution.   11:02.5

Strophe 31

1) T/F- The boy has a difficult time finding the factory.

2) T/F- The boy has to wait outside the factory before going in.

3) Once inside the building, where does the boy go?

The boy follows the sign with the arrow to locate the right room.   11:32.4

Strophe 32

1) T/F- The receptionist is busy typing.

2) What is her reaction to the boy?

The Signer describes the receptionist's puffed hairdo.

11:37.0

The Signer takes the role of the receptionist while the boy reaches out his hand to get her attention.

11:48.0

Strophe 33

1) How does the boy communicate with the receptionist?

2) What exactly does he tell her?

3) What is the receptionist's response to the boy's request?

Strophe 34

1) T/F- The guards force the boy out of the factory.

2) Y/N- Does he come back in two days?

3) What is the receptionist's response regarding job openings this time?

Time Code

The Signer takes the role of the boy and stands rigidly in front of the receptionist waiting for her response.

12:32.0

Strophe 35

1) Does the boy return to the factory many times or one time?

2) T/F- The receptionist gives the boy an application to fill out.

Time Code

The application form appears highly detailed to the boy.   12:48.5

Strophe 36

1) What is the first item on the form?

2) What item is answered incorrectly?

Strophe 36 (cont'd)   Time Code

The boy moves down to another item on the   13:00.2
application form.

The Signer takes the role of the boy and   13:01.3
narrates about his idea to use the
hunchback's address.

Strophe 37

1) Which question is the boy unable to answer?

2) T/F- The boy is able to sign his name at the end of the form.

3) What does the receptionist do with the form?

Strophe 37 (cont'd)

The boy leaves an entire section of the application form blank.

13:15.4

Strophe 38

1) Y/N- Does the boy get the job immediately?

2) How does the receptionist contact the boss?

3) What color is the boss' shirt?

Strophe 39

1) T/F- The boss is able to communicate through fingerspelling.

2) Why does the boss show the boy a deaf peddler's card?

Strophe 40

1) How does the boy know that he is hired?

2) T/F- The reaction of the secretary is restrained.

3) T/F- The boy is elated when he is hired for the job.

Strophe 41

1) T/F- The factory has one big plane in it.

2) What other work is being done besides welding?
         a) a huge piston is being lowered
         b) there is drilling being done
         c) a crane is lowering a big pipe
         d) a piston is being welded

Time Code

The Signer outlines the safety glasses on the welding mask.　　14:24.4

Strophe 41 (cont'd)   Time Code

The Signer describes the welding process with bright sparks flying.   14:29.8

Strophe 42

1) Where is the boy's work station?
      a) in the basement, straight down from the receptionist's office
      b) far from the welding station
      c) in a corner
      d) b and c

2) T/F- The boy sits in a small booth by himself.

3) What does the boss show the boy inside the booth?

The Signer describes the factory full of machinery noises.   14:39.5

Strophe 42 (cont'd)   Time Code

The Signer describes a collection of nuts and   15:02.4
bolts in front of the boy.

Strophe 43

1) T/F- The boy receives a demonstration on how to do his job.

2) T/F- The boy uses a screwdriver in his assembly.

The Signer takes the role of the boss and   15:12.4
demonstrates the work to the boy.

Strophe 44

1) T/F- The second part that the boy works on is the same as the first.

2) Y/N- Does he know what the part is used for?

Time Code

The Signer takes the role of the boy and narrates not knowing the function of his assembly work. It does not matter to him.

15:29.5

Strophe 45

1) T/F- The boy's work is slow.

2) How does the boss praise the boy for his work?
        a) He pats the boy's back.
        b) He smiles and fingerspells "good."
        c) He writes a nice note.
        d) Both a and b.

The Signer takes the role of the boy and narrates to describe his high productivity.

15:38.3

169

Strophe 46

1) T/F- The boy sees his co-worker listening to music.

2) Where is the co-worker?

3) Y/N- Does the boy report his co-worker to his boss?

Time Code

The Signer describes a radio blaring.   15:54.4

Strophe 47

1) T/F- The second co-worker is chatting with another worker and laughing.

2) T/F- The boy attempts to participate in his co-workers' conversation.

The Signer takes the role of the boy and has   16:11.6
to endure his working conditions.

Background: Deaf People and Employment

In the narrative, the boy character was determined to find employment, and only with persistence did he get a job at the aircraft factory. This coincides with the historical fact that during the World War II, deaf people were well received in the industry, and there they have established excellent work records.[52] One should note that during wartime, women and other minorities have made great strides in the workplace, and apparently, it is the same for deaf people. Unfortunately, for most of history and continuing to be true today, deaf people as a group suffer higher unemployment and underemployment as compared with the rest of workers in the United States. The earning discrepancies between the deaf and general populations have, in fact, worsened in the latter part of this century and that the parity between the two groups has yet to be realized.[53] Recall from the preceding chapter, the protagonist was given the lead to the aircraft factory, but was told that deaf people could not find a job there. In a real situation, the deaf community in a given city is often well aware of certain industries that would not try to employ deaf people, but according to the narrative, the protagonist defied the odds and went ahead to find employment in the aircraft factory. In many cases, deaf people have experienced discrimination related to prejudices and communication barriers in either finding or maintaining employment.

After the Civil War, deaf people were specifically prohibited from taking the examination needed for any federal government job, but the regulations were eventually reversed.[54] However, in certain industries, the working prospects were favorable for deaf people, and one notable example is the Goodyear and Firestone rubber companies operating in Akron, Ohio. During World War II and the following years, there was a large number of deaf employees in these two companies. Printing also became a popular occupation for deaf people, and many schools for the deaf had developed printing as part of vocational training for their students.[55] Linotyping was a popular trade among deaf printers until photocomposition began to replace linotype.[56] It is not the ever-changing technology that affected the job opportunities for deaf people, but rather that the nature of jobs has changed from manual to service-oriented. That is, the increase in service, sales, and clerical occupations with their emphasis on communication has worked to the disadvantage of deaf people.[57]

For the protagonist in the narrative, the assembly line occupation at the aircraft factory is suitable as it requires minimal communication with hearing people. Moreover, the employer in the narrative was able to fingerspell, and that has made communication possible in the workplace. At present, there is progress in workplaces where signed language classes are offered. Interpreters are also now more available, and in certain companies like IBM, they are used extensively, for example, during work-related meetings. The deaf employees are able to follow the weekly meetings when they could not in the past. Much work is still needed to ensure that deaf people have better job opportunities as well as better work conditions. The recent passage of the Americans with Disabilities Act by the United States Congress may mark the movement towards the needed changes in the American industry and its treatment toward the deaf people.

LITERARY QUESTIONS

1) What does the boy's persistence at finding employment in the aircraft factory tell us about his character?

2) Describe the cultural conflict created in how the boy tried to get the receptionist's attention. Do you think this accounts for the receptionist's particular behavior towards the boy?

3) What is the irony of the boss having an ABC card?

4) Discuss the differences in the working conditions of the deaf and hearing workers in the factory. If you were the boss yourself, what would you do to improve the working conditions of deaf workers?

• • •

CHAPTER 5
THE ACCIDENT

CHAPTER 5		
THE ACCIDENT		
Topic Unit		
13	14	15
Lunch Time	Shortcut to the Cafeteria	The Boy Gets Stuck
Strophes		
48-51	52-55	56-60

Comprehension Check

Strophe 48

1) How does the boy find out that it is lunch time?
      a) He is tapped by a co-worker.
      b) He realizes that the co-workers are gone.
      c) He feels some vibrations from the lunch bell.
      d) b and c.

2) Y/N- Does he see a crowd of workers rushing to lunch?

Time Code

The Signer takes the role of the boy and narrates the problems at work—the worst part being the situation with the lunch bell.

16:16.7

Strophe 48 (cont'd)   Time Code

The Signer takes the role of the boy and narrates of his shortcoming–that he is deaf and oblivious to the lunch bell.

16:23.1

Strophe 49

1) T/F- The boy is trying to catch up with the rest of his workers.

2) Where is the cafeteria?

3) T/F- The boy is last in line.

The Signer takes the role of the boy who is out of breath.

16:45.7

174

Strophe 50

1) T/F- Lunch is served cafeteria-style.

2) Why does the boy want the servers to rush?
   a) He is so hungry.
   b) He is tired and wants to sit down.
   c) He is late and has a limited amount of time.
   d) He is excited about trying the food.

3) Y/N- Does the boy have time to enjoy his meal?

Strophe 51

1) Y/N- Does somebody check on the boy?

2) What happens to the boy after every lunch?

Time Code

The Signer describes that the cafeteria is empty when the boy rushes out.

17:06.0

175

Strophe 51 (cont'd)   Time Code

The Signer narrates about the chair nearly   17:09.7
tipping over when the boy rushes to sit down
at his work station.

Strophe 52

1) T/F- The boy asks his boss for permission to leave his work station.

2) What does the boy find as he goes to the bathroom?

3) How are the gears set up?
        a) in a large container on the floor
        b) there are two broken gears lying on the floor
        c) in a stack
        d) there are grinding gears through an opening in the floor

The Signer takes the role of the boy and   17:25.5
narrates his need to go to the bathroom.

Strophe 53

1) T/F- The boy takes the shortcut because he sees that his co-workers are leaving for lunch.

2) Y/N- When the boy lands, do his legs hurt?

Time Code

The Signer takes the role of the boy and narrates about his decision to jump through the shortcut.

17:59.1

The floor and gears rush past the boy as he jumps down–signed from the boy's perspective.

18:05.6

Strophe 54

1) T/F- The boy still finds himself last in the lunch line.

2) Y/N- Does he have plenty of time to finish his lunch?

3) Y/N- Does the boss approach the boy and discipline him for his jumping action?

Time Code

The Signer takes the role of the buffet server   18:16.5
and responds to the boy after he jumps
through the shortcut.

Strophe 55

1) Y/N- Does the boy jump through the shortcut every day?

2) How do the co-workers react?
       a) They go to tell the boss.
       b) They protest to the boy.
       c) They do nothing and leave the boy alone.
       d) a and b

Strophe 56

1) Why does the boy get stuck in the gears this time?

2) Where exactly do the gears grab-hold?

Time Code

The Signer describes the buttons bursting off   18:47.2
the boy's shirt in the mishap.

Strophe 57

1) T/F- The gears throw the boy out.

2) What part of the boy's body is scraped?

3) How do the co-workers respond this time?
       a) They continue rushing to the cafeteria.
       b) They stop and cannot decide what to do.
       c) They rush to find the boss.
       d) None of the above.

Strophe 57 (cont'd)

The Signer takes the role of narrator and describes the power and lights being turned off.   18:59.3

The Signer describes smoke coming out of the machinery and its gears when it is stopped.   19:01.2

The Signer describes the boy's body entangled in the gears.   19:03.2

Strophe 58

1) Y/N- Is a doctor quickly summoned?

2) T/F- The boy is put on a chair after he is pulled from the gears.

3) T/F- The boy is surrounded by his co-workers.

Strophe 59

1) T/F- One of the co-workers goes ahead and examines the boy first.

2) How does the doctor examine the boy?

3) What is the result of the doctor's diagnosis?

Time Code

The Signer describes the light reflected from the doctor's equipment.

19:21.4

Strophe 60

1) When the boss finds out about the accident, what does he do?

2) T/F- The boy's body is sent to a funeral home.

	Time Code
The Signer narrates that the boy's body is covered with a sheet.	19:56.4

Background: Audism

In this chapter, we see the protagonist encounter another subtle barrier that would not exist if he were a hearing person. An example of this barrier is the lunch bell. While it may appear trivial to a hearing person who takes this device for granted, something like a simple lunch bell is one of life's many obstacles for a deaf person. The basic purpose of this mechanism is to alert a group of people by means of sound; it thus excludes all people who cannot hear. Such exclusion may be unintentional or intentional. However, whether intentional or not, the use of sound as the only mechanism for regulating working hours establishes an inequality between deaf and hearing workers. This turns out to be an institutional arrangement that discriminates in favor of hearing people and against deaf people.

The notion that one is superior based on one's ability to hear or behave in the manner of one who hears. Audism, it is argued, has crept into the consciousness of people–both hearing and deaf–so that they believe that in order to succeed in society, they are obliged to behave in accordance with institutional arrangements.[58]

The notion of audism has been compared to racism and sexism in terms of the way in which the majority deals with minorities. All institutional arrangements, beliefs, values, behaviors and attitudes are determined and naturalized in favor of the majority group over the minority group. It may be especially difficult for hearing people to grasp the concept of audism because they have taken their capability to hear for granted. That is, the ability to hear seems to them the only way to live, and they may not realize the magnitude and implications of this arrangement.[59]

Oftentimes, the audistic behavior of hearing people is unintentional, but there are cases of people intentionally asserting their auditory supremacy over deaf people. The setting in which the most prevalent practice of audism occurs is the educational institution.[60] The curriculum and instruction is in the notion of the supremacy of the English language and mainstream American hearing culture and pay minimal attention to deaf culture and the language of deaf people. American Sign Language has been considered the reason that some deaf people are unable to learn spoken English. This orientation towards the supremacy of the English language and mainstream hearing culture and the stigmatization of ASL and deaf culture is not only endemic among educators of the deaf, but includes the entire human service sector dealing with deafness, such as audiology, speech therapy, medicine, psychology, and social work.[61]

It is important to realize that audism may appear in two forms: covert and overt. The human service sector is filled with people trained to treat and view deaf people as suffering from a pathology and in need of rehabilitation. In overt audism, deaf people are regarded as inferior, incomplete, and unhealthy.

There are also many instances of covert audism, especially in the case of people who do not know or have not had any contact with the deaf community. They view being deaf as a human calamity and believe that deaf people are in a steady state of despair. Unconsciously, they participate in an institutional arrangement that excludes deaf people from having equal access to the world around them, in much the same way as the hearing co-workers in the story. Many hearing people participate in institutional arrangements that are covertly audistic without being aware of the audism. These institutional arrangements do not make provision for alternative sources of access for deaf people. They include practices and institutions such as public announcements only on the radio, public telephones, etc.

Audism, while it may still be on the rise, appears to have reached a plateau (at least on the surface) as a result of deaf awareness of and resistance to it. There is increased public awareness of deafness and the nature of ASL as a language, as well as legislative acts that allow for more access to societal institutions through the provision of different services, such as interpreting, relay services, and captioning on television.

LITERARY QUESTIONS

1) Why is it significant and symbolic that the boy is always the last to know it is lunch time and also the last in line?

2) What does the boy's decision to jump through the shortcut tell us about his character? How do you compare this action with the protagonist running away from home as occurred earlier in the narrative?

3) If you were the boy, what alternative(s) would you consider over jumping through the shortcut? Remember that you are deaf, and the boss can only fingerspell.

• • •

CHAPTER 6
THE SECOND LIFE

CHAPTER 6
THE SECOND LIFE

Topic Unit	
16 The Boy Lives	17 Return to Work
Strophes	
61-66	67-71

Comprehension Check

Strophe 61

1) T/F- The boy is left lying on a gurney.

2) Y/N- Does he wake up with the sheet still covering his face?

3) What does the boy see on the ceiling above him?

Time Code

The Signer narrates to describe the setting with a number of corpses lying next to each other.

20:08.7

185

Strophe 61 (cont'd)   Time Code

The Signer takes the role of the boy and asks   20:17.8
the audience, "Can you imagine?"

Strophe 62

1) What does the boy see next to him?

2) T/F- The boy gets up and finds himself limping.

3) Why does he have to wrap himself in a sheet?

Strophe 63

1) What does the boy find when he peeks through the window?
    a) a sleeping mortician
    b) two morticians, busy working
    c) work being conducted on a corpse
    d) b and c

2) T/F- The boy rushes to the door.

Strophe 63 (cont'd)

The Signer takes the role of the corpse being pumped with silicone.

21:03.1

The Signer describes the mortician powdering the corpse's face.

21:05.0

Strophe 64

1) T/F- The boy attempts to avoid the morticians.

2) What does the boy do that causes the morticians to scream?

Strophe 64 (cont'd)   Time Code

The Signer takes the role of the boy and   21:18.2
narrates about resorting to talk because
he had no pen and paper.

Strophe 65

1) T/F- The boy goes straight to the hospital with no stops along the way.

2) What did they do to his leg while he is in the hospital?

3) What dilemma does he face while in the hospital?
   a) He is stuck there without an interpreter.
   b) He does not have insurance.
   c) He cannot call his boss.
   d) b and c

The Signer takes the role of the boy who is   21:47.9
bedridden, with his leg elevated.

Strophe 66

1) T/F- The boy tells the doctor that he has decided to leave the hospital.

2) What does the boy use to leave the hospital?

3) Y/N- Does he have to sign something to leave the hospital?

Time Code

The Signer takes the role of the doctor and releases the boy.

21:51.3

Strophe 67

1) T/F- The trolley riders stare at the boy's condition.

2) When the trolley stops, how does the boy get off?

3) Is he able to enter the factory?

Strophe 68

1) Who does the boy stop to greet?

2) How does this person react to his greeting?

3) T/F- The boy stays in the room for an half-hour.

Strophe 69

1) What is the boss doing before the boy gets his attention?

2) What happens after the boss sees the boy?
   - a) He screams the boy's name.
   - b) The lunch bell rings.
   - c) All the workers rush to see the boy.
   - d) a and c

Time Code

The Signer describes the clamp on the clipboard.

22:42.6

190

Strophe 70

1) How does the boy tell his story of what happened?
        a) The boss interprets for the boy.
        b) Another deaf co-worker interprets for the boy.
        c) The boy writes an explanation down on paper.
        d) None of the above.

Strophe 71

1) The boss is impressed by the boy; what is the direct result of this?

2) Who does the boy see unexpectedly?

3) T/F- The ending of this story is happy.

Time Code

The Signer takes the role of the boss and calls deaf people to work at the factory.

23:13.0

191

LITERARY QUESTIONS

1) Why is the boy in the morgue if he is not really dead?

2) How do you account for the pattern of the boy not asking for help (e.g., not asking someone to call the boss from the hospital)? Do you think this pattern also occurs in the protagonist's interaction with deaf people?

3) What is the boy's attitude when he returns to the factory? Why?

4) What is the irony in the fact that the president of the deaf club now works in the aircraft factory?

• • •

END NOTES

[1] C. Ketelhut & B. Bahan, 1991a.

[2] Ibid.

[3] Ibid.

[4] Ibid.

[5] M. Harvey, 1989.

[6] R. Freeman, et al., 1975.

[7] D. Moores, 1987.
   R. Freeman, et al., 1981.

[8] M. Harvey, 1989.

[9] M. Vernon & J. Andrew, 1990.

[10] S. Quigley & R. Kretschmer, 1982.

[11] C. Erting, et al., 1990.

[12] G. Becker, 1987.

[13] J. Woodward, 1982.

[14] V. Charrow & R. Wilbur, 1989, p. 103.

[15] H. Markowicz, 1980.

[16] V. Charrow & R. Wilbur, 1989, p. 105.

[17] R. Meier, 1991.

[18] S. Supalla, 1990.

[19] S. Davies, 1991.

[20] R. Johnson, et al., 1989.

[21] V. Charrow & R. Wilbur, 1989.

[22] R. Johnson, et al., 1989.

[23] D. Moores, 1987.
    H. Lane, 1984.

[24] J. Van Cleve & B. Crouch, 1989.

[25] Ibid.

[26] Ibid.

[27] J. Van Cleve & B. Crouch, 1989.
    J. Gannon, 1981.

[28] J. Van Cleve & B. Crouch, 1989.

[29] Ibid.

[30] A. Neisser, 1983.

[31] G. Becker, 1987.

[32] C. Erting, 1987.

[33] M. Harvey, 1989, p. 46.

[34] C. Erting, 1987.

[35] J. Schein, 1989.

[36] G. Becker, 1987.

[37] C. Padden & T. Humphries, 1988.
C. Erting, 1987.

[38] C. Padden & T. Humphries, 1988.

[39] C. Erting, 1987.

[40] C. Padden & T. Humphries, 1988.

[41] L. Aldridge, 1984, p. 126.

[42] J. Mendelsohn & B. Fairchild, 1984, p. 113.

[43] K. Meadow-Orlans, 1987, p. 53-54.

[44] I. Balkany, 1993.

[45] H. Lane, 1992.

[46] I. Balkany, 1993.

[47] C. Ketelhut & B. Bahan, 1991b.

[48] Ibid.

[49] P. Higgins, 1980.
J. Van Cleve, 1987.

[50] J. Schein, 1989.

[51] Ibid., p. 87.

[52] J. Van Cleve & B. Crouch, 1989.

[53] J. Schein, 1989.

[54] J. Van Cleve & B. Crouch, 1989.

[55] Ibid.

[56] J. Gannon, 1981.

[57] J. Van Cleve & B. Crouch, 1989.

[58] T. Humphries, 1977.

[59] S. Nover, 1993.

[60] S. Nover, 1993.
H. Lane, 1992.

[61] H. Lane, 1992.

• • •

REFERENCES

Aldridge, L. (1984). Surviving adolescence. In G. Anderson & D. Watson (Eds.), *The habilitation and rehabilitation of deaf adolescents*. Proceedings of the National Conference on the Habilitation and Rehabilitation of Deaf Adolescents (pp. 123-133).

Balkany, T. (1993). A brief perspective on cochlear implants. *The New England Journal of Medicine, 328*, 281-282.

Becker, G. (1987). Lifelong socialization and adaptive behavior of deaf people. In P. Higgins & J. Nash (Eds.), *Understanding deafness socially* (pp. 59-79). Springfield, IL: Charles C. Thomas Publisher.

Bragg, B., & Bergman, E. (1981). *Tales from a Clubroom*. Washington, DC: Gallaudet College Press.

Charrow, V., & Wilbur, R. (1989). The deaf child as a linguistic minority. In S. Wilcox (Ed.), *American deaf culture: An anthology* (pp. 103-115). Silver Spring, MD: Linstok Press.

Davies, S. (1991). Bilingual education of deaf children in Sweden and Denmark: Strategies for transition and implementation. *Sign Language Studies, 71*, 161-195.

Erting, C., Prezioso, C., & O'Grady-Hynes, M. (1990). The interactional context of deaf mother-infant communication. In V. Volterra & C. Erting (Eds.), *From gesture to language in hearing and deaf children* (pp. 97-106). Heidelberg: Springer-Verlag.

Erting, C. (1987). Cultural conflict in a school for deaf children. In P. Higgins & J. Nash (Eds.), *Understanding deafness socially* (pp. 123-150). Springfield, IL: Charles C. Thomas Publisher.

Freeman, R., Malkin, S., & Hastings, J. (1975). Psychosocial problems of deaf children and their families: A comparative study. *American Annals of the Deaf, 120*, 391-405.

Freeman, R., Carbin, C., & Boese, R. (1981). *Can't your child hear? A guide for those who care about deaf children.* Austin, TX: Pro-Ed.

Gannon, J. (1981). *Deaf heritage: A narrative history of deaf America.* Silver Springs, MD: National Association of the Deaf.

Harvey, M. (1989). *Psychotherapy with deaf and hard of hearing persons: A systematic model.* Hillsdale, NJ: Lawrence Erlbaum Associates.

Higgins, P. (1980). *Outsiders in a hearing world: A sociology of deafness.* Beverly Hills, CA: Sage.

Humphries, T. (1977). *Communicating across cultures (deaf/hearing) and language learning.* Unpublished doctoral dissertation, Cincinnati, OH: Union Graduate School.

Johnson, R., Liddell, S., & Erting, C. (1989). *Unlocking the curriculum: Principles for achieving access in deaf education.* Gallaudet Research Institute Working Paper, 89-3. Washington, DC: Gallaudet University.

Ketelhut, C., & Bahan, B. (1991a). *The Eagle Fable: A literary analysis.* Unpublished manuscript, Boston University, Boston.

Ketelhut, C., & Bahan, B. (1991b). *For a Decent Living* by Sam Supalla: A literary analysis. Unpublished manuscript, Boston University, Boston.

Lane, H. (1992). *The mask of benevolence: Disabling the deaf community.* New York, NY: Alfred A. Knopf.

Lane, H. (1984). *When the mind hears: A history of the deaf.* New York, NY: Random House.

Markowicz, H. (1980). Some sociolinguistic considerations of American Sign Language. In W. Stokoe (Ed.), *Sign and culture*, (pp. 267-294). Silver Spring, MD: Linstok Press.

Meadow-Orlans, K. (1987). Understanding deafness: Socialization of children and youth. In P. C. Higgins & J. E. Nash (Eds.), *Understanding deafness socially* (pp. 29-57). Springfield, IL: Charles C. Thomas Publisher.

Meier, R. (1991). Language acquisition by deaf children. *American Scientist, 79,* 60-70.

Mendelsohn, J., & Fairchild, B. (1984). Year of challenge: Parents, adolescence and deafness. In G. Anderson & D. Watson (Eds.), *The habilitation and rehabilitation of deaf adolescents.* Proceedings of the National Conference on Habilitation and Rehabilitation of Deaf Adolescents. (pp. 110-122).

Moores, D. (1987). *Educating the deaf: Psychology, principles, and practices.* (3rd ed.). Boston, MA: Houghton-Mifflin.

Neisser, A. (1983). *The other side of silence: Sign language and the deaf community in America.* New York, NY: Alfred A. Knopf.

Nover, S. (1993). *Our voices, our vision: Politics of deaf education.* Paper presented at the Convention of American Instructors of the Deaf and Conference of Educational Administrators Serving the Deaf.

Padden, C. & Humphries, T. (1988). *Deaf in America: Voices from a culture.* Cambridge, MA: Harvard University Press.

Quigley, S., & Kretchmer, R. (1982). *The education of deaf children.* Baltimore, MD: University Park Press.

Schein, J. (1989). *At home among strangers.* Washington, DC: Gallaudet University Press.

Supalla, S. (1990). *Segmentation of Manually Coded English: Problems in the mapping of English in the visual/gestural mode.* Unpublished doctoral dissertation, University of Illinois, Urbana-Champaign.

Van Cleve, J. (1987). Paternalism. In J. Van Cleve (Ed.), *Gallaudet encyclopedia of deaf people and deafness* (pp. 70-71). New York, NY: McGraw-Hill.

Van Cleve, J., & Crouch, B. (1989). *A place of their own: Creating the deaf community in America.* Washington, DC: Gallaudet University Press.

Vernon, M., & Andress, J. (1990). *The psychology of deafness: Understanding deaf and hard of hearing people.* New York, NY: Longman.

Woodward, J. (1982). *How you gonna get to heaven if you can't talk to Jesus? On depathologizing deafness.* Silver Spring, MD: TJ Publishers.

• • •

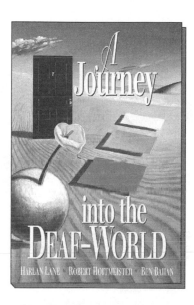

MORE TITLES FOR ADVANCED ASL STUDENTS

An instant classic when first staged, the play Tales from a Clubroom brings to life characters and situations that remain significant to today's audience. The drama unfolds in a familiar enviroment to those in the Deaf World, offering candid views of the language, culture, and experiences of the Deaf community. Crafted by pioneers of Deaf Theatre, Bernard Bragg and Eugene Bergman, this masterwork continues to impact readers and viewers with its humor, poignant drama, and gratifying portrayals of true-to-life deaf individuals.

Tales from a Clubroom
Bernard Bragg and Eugene Bergman

The Treasure showcases the original works of the renowned Deaf poet Ella Mae Lentz. This native-daughter of the Deaf community gives passionate expression to personal and social observations in exquisite ASL. Through the powerful imagery and rhythms of ASL, Ella creates an intimate portrayal of both her own life's joys and challenges and her community's bonds and clashes.

The Treasure
ASL Poems by Ella Mae Lentz

Clayton Valli, creative and celebrated ASL poet, had a dream to see ASL poetry thrive and grow. In this collection of twenty-one poems, the breadth and beauty of ASL is showcased as a diverse group of signers recite works by Valli. This collection is an invaluable resource for the study and enjoyment of ASL poetry. This DVD format is simple to use and gives viewers the flexibility to navigate easily between poems.

ASL Poetry
Selected works of Clayton Valli

A to Z: ABC Stories in ASL showcases six gifted performers: Ben Bahan, Linsay Darnall, Jr., Stefanie Ellis-Gonzales, Ben Jarashow, CJ Jones, and Brian J. Morrison. Using imagination and skill, they create a visual feast. At once delightful, humorous, inspiring, and simply amazing, this collection of ABC stories is sure to entertain. This DVD is a valuable resource for storytellers, teachers, and students, and enjoyable for anyone who delights in ASL stories.

A to Z: ABC Stories in ASL
Directed by Ben Bahan & Ben Jarashow

DawnSignPress ◆ 6130 Nancy Ridge Drive, San Diego, California 92121-3223 ◆ www.dawnsign.com